Standard Bible Story Readers

BOOK SIX
(The Fifth Reader)

BY
LILLIE A. FARIS
First Grade Critic Teacher, College of Education of
Ohio University, Athens, O.

Illustrated by O. A. STEMLER and BESS BRUCE CLEAVELAND

———————— ❖ ————————

THE STANDARD PUBLISHING COMPANY
CINCINNATI, O.

PREFACE

It would be absolutely impossible for any one to improve upon the Bible story. It is best told by the original author. The language is pure, classical and far above our poor power to criticize, and the intendment of this series of Bible Story Readers has been only to simplify words and phrases which were beyond the child's understanding; it has been to help the child secure the background necessary for a complete understanding of the story. The material has been selected with the hope that the children will be so interested in the few outstanding stories which have been given that they will want to read the Bible for themselves and find still other stories which are quite as entrancing as the ones found in this series of readers.

The purpose of introducing here and there through each of the readers a choice Psalm or bit of Scripture is to prove to the child that the Bible itself is full of charming expressions and stories. Great care has been taken to increase the amount of such gems as the succeeding books were issued, and, as BOOK SIX finds its place in the hands of the child, it will be noted that it is replete with stories told in Bible language. The matchless parables of Jesus are given in His own phraseology; they are compelling, and one does not care to comment upon them lest their beauty be blighted.

BOOK SIX also contains its touches of patriotism and home life, and includes a very few exquisite bits of poetry which always make their appeal to the sixth-grade child.

Grateful acknowledgment is made to Houghton, Mifflin & Company for their kind permission to use the poems "The Chamber Over the Gate," "The Ship of State," "The Arrow and the Song" and "The Builders," by Henry W. Longfellow; "The Chambered Nautilus," by Oliver Wendell Holmes; "The Captain's Daughter," by James T. Fields; "The Sandpiper," by Celia Thaxter; "The Eternal Goodness," "King Solomon and the Ants" and "Knowest Thou the Ordinances of Heaven," by John Greenleaf Whittier; and to Berton Braley, with whom special arrangement was made for use of his poem "Let Me Stand and Cheer."

The author also expresses her sincere gratitude to the publishers and their skilled mechanics who have labored to make the work attractive; to the artists who gave us their best efforts, and to every one who has aided in any way the publication of this series of readers.

And now to the books we say: "Go to every country; go to the hands of every child and help him to understand that God is God, that He is an ever-present Guide, and that all good things are gifts from this loving heavenly Father; help him to understand his duty toward this loving heavenly Father and to know that, so long as he tries to understand and do His commands,

> " 'God's in His heaven;
> All's right with the world.' "

CONTENTS

5

MAJESTIC SWEETNESS

Majestic sweetness sits enthroned
   Upon the Saviour's brow;
His head with radiant glories crowned,
   His lips with grace o'erflow.

No mortal can with Him compare
   Among the sons of men;
Fairer is He than all the fair
   That fill the heavenly train.

He saw me plunged in deep distress,
   And flew to my relief;
For me He bore the shameful cross,
   And carried all my grief.

To Him I owe my life and breath,
   And all the joys I have:
He makes me triumph over death,
   And saves me from the grave.

Since from His bounty I receive
   Such proofs of love divine,
Had I a thousand hearts to give,
   Lord, they should all be Thine.

—*Samuel Stennett.*

THE VANITY OF LIFE

I said, I will take heed to my ways,
That I sin not with my tongue:
I will keep my mouth with a bridle,
While the wicked is before me.

I was dumb with silence, I held my peace even from
good;
And my sorrow was stirred.
My heart was hot within me;
While I was musing the fire burned;
Then spake I with my tongue:
Jehovah, make me to know mine end,
And the measure of my days, what it is;
Let me know how frail I am.

Behold, Thou hast made my days as handbreadths;
And my lifetime is as nothing before Thee:
Surely every man at his best estate is altogether
vanity.

Surely every man walketh in a vain show;
Surely they are disquieted in vain:

He heapeth up riches, and knoweth not who shall
  gather them.

And now, Lord, what wait I for?
My hope is in Thee.
Deliver me from all my transgressions:
Make me not the reproach of the foolish.

I was dumb, I opened not my mouth;
Because Thou didst it.
Remove Thy stroke away from me:
I am consumed by the blow of Thy hand.
When Thou with rebukes dost correct man for
  iniquity,
Thou makest his beauty to consume away like a moth:
Surely every man is vanity.

Hear my prayer, O Jehovah, and give ear unto
  my cry;
Hold not Thy peace at my tears:
For I am a stranger with Thee,
A sojourner, as all my fathers were.
Oh spare me, that I may recover strength,
Before I go hence, and be no more.

—Psalm 39.

11

THE ARROW AND
THE SONG

I shot an arrow into the air,
It fell to earth, I knew not where;
For, so swiftly it flew, the sight
Could not follow it in its flight.

I breathed a song into the air,
It fell to earth, I knew not where;
For who has sight so keen and strong
That it can follow the flight of song?

Long, long afterward, in an oak
I found the arrow, still unbroke;
And the song, from beginning to end,
I found again in the heart of a friend.

—Henry W. Longfellow.

THE SHIP OF STATE

Thou, too, sail on, O Ship of State!
Sail on, O Union, strong and great!
Humanity, with all its fears,
With all the hopes of future years,
Is hanging breathless on thy fate!
We know what Master laid thy keel,
What Workman wrought thy ribs of steel,
Who made each mast, and sail, and rope;
What anvils rang, what hammers beat,
In what a forge and what a heat
Were forged the anchors of thy hope!
Fear not each sudden sound and shock—
'Tis of the wave, and not the rock;
'Tis but the flapping of the sail,
And not a rent made by the gale!
In spite of rock and tempest roar,
In spite of false lights on the shore,
Sail on, nor fear to breast the sea!
Our hearts, our hopes, are all with thee.
Our hearts, our hopes, our prayers, our tears,
Our faith, triumphant o'er our fears,
Are all with thee, are all with thee!

—Henry W. Longfellow.

A QUEST FOR A WIFE

In the far eastern country of Palestine, it was not the custom for a young man to call upon a lady whom he admired; it was not even the custom for him to ask her to be his wife, even though he might want her ever so much. A father always selected his son's wife, and so it happened that when the good old man Abraham wanted his son Isaac to get married he called a trusty servant to him and told him to go back into his own home country and find there a wife for his son Isaac.

Abraham gave his servant orders to be very careful about the woman he should choose. The servant got ready to start back to Abraham's old home, and he prepared great presents to carry to his master's people. There were ten camels loaded with good things, and the long journey to the city of Nahor was begun.

The way was long, the road was rough, and the men must have been very tired by the time they came to the city gate. When they finally did come to the city, the servant made the camels to kneel down by a well of water. It was just the time

of the evening when the women went out to draw the water, and the servant was sure he would find a good girl to become Isaac's wife.

The old servant had a pretty hard task on his hands, and he asked God to help him. He said: "Behold, I am standing by the fountain of water, and the daughters of the men of the city are coming out to draw water: and let it come to pass, that the damsel to whom I shall say, Let down thy pitcher, I pray thee, that I may drink; and she shall say, Drink, and I will give thy camels drink also: let the same be she that thou hast appointed for thy servant Isaac; and thereby shall I know that thou hast showed kindness unto my master."

Even before the servant was done praying, a beautiful girl came close to the well. She carried a pitcher on her head. The servant saw that she was a kind-hearted girl. He watched her as she let the pitcher down into the well and as she drew it up again. As she turned away he went up to her and asked her for a drink. He had already made up his mind that the woman he chose for Isaac must be very kind-hearted, and

16

he was very pleased when she gave him the
water. And Rebekah, for that was her name,
said to him, "I will draw water for thy camels
also, until they have done drinking." She hur-
ried and drew the water and carried it to the
trough and ran back to the well for more.

All the time the servant kept watching her and hop-
ing that she was the one who was to be Isaac's
wife. After the camels had done drinking, Abraham's servant gave her some of the lovely presents he had brought. There was a gold ring,
and there were two beautiful bracelets. Then
he asked her what her father's name was, and
if she thought he might remain at their home
all night. She told him who she was, and as-
sured him that he would be welcome.

Rebekah ran to her home and told the family about
the man at the fountain. The father and mother
and brother told her to go and invite the man
and those who were with him to come to the house.

When the men came up to the house they found that
Rebekah's father and brother had prepared a
place for them and the camels. They gave the
camels food, then gave the servant water so

that he and his men might wash their feet and rest. Then they set food before the men, but Abraham's servant did not eat; he said, "I will not eat until after I have told you my errand." And Rebekah's father said, "Say on."

The old servant told the whole story of his long trip, of the stop at the well, of Jehovah's promise to help him find the right wife for Isaac, and of Rebekah's kindness to him. Then he asked if Rebekah might go back with him to become the wife of Isaac. Rebekah's father and mother and brother loved her very dearly, but they were willing for her to go. The servant gave all the family the presents he had brought, and made ready to return. And Rebekah and her maidens rode upon the camels, and followed the man until they came to a field where Isaac was watching.

When Rebekah saw him she asked the old servant who he was, and the man answered, "It is my master." Then she took her veil and covered herself until after she had met Isaac. When Rebekah's story was told to him he was very much pleased, and took her home to his mother's tent, to become his wife.

GOD OUR REFUGE

God is our refuge and strength,
A very present help in trouble.
Therefore we will not fear, though the earth do
change,
And though the mountains be shaken into the heart of
the seas;
Though the waters thereof roar and be troubled,
Though the mountains tremble with the swelling
thereof.

There is a river, the streams whereof make glad the
city of God,
The holy place of the tabernacles of the Most High.
God is in the midst of her; she shall not be moved:
God will help her, and that right early.

.　　.　　.　　.　　.　　.

Be still, and know that I am God:
I will be exalted among the nations, I will be exalted
in the earth.
Jehovah of hosts is with us;
The God of Jacob is our refuge.

—Psalm 46.

20

HOME, SWEET HOME

John Howard Payne   Sir Henry Bishop

1. 'Mid pleas-ures and pal-a-ces though we may roam, Be it ev-er so
2. I gaze on the moon as I tread the drear wild, And feel that my
3. An ex-ile from home, splendor daz-zles in vain; Oh, give me my

hum-ble, there's no place like home; A charm from the skies seems to hal-low us
moth-er now thinks of her child; As she looks on that moon from our own cot-tage
low-ly thatched cot-tage a-gain; The birds singing gai-ly, that came at my

there, Which, seek thro' the world, is ne'er met with else-where. Home, home,
door, Thro' the wood-bine whose fragrance shall cheer me no more. Home, home,
call; Give me them, and that peace of mind, dear-er than all. Home, home,

sweet, sweet home, Be it ev-er so hum-ble, there's no place like home.

SETTLING A QUARREL

It was a good many years after Isaac and Rebekah had been married before there were any little children in the home. At last two baby boys came—twins they were—and their names were Esau and Jacob. They were just as different from each other as day is from night; and, of course, as they grew older, they enjoyed different things. Esau loved to hunt, and grew to be very skillful. Nothing pleased him better than to roam around through the fields all day. But Jacob was quiet and loved to stay around the home.

After the two boys had grown to be men, Jacob played a trick on Esau. It was this way: Esau was just a little bit older than Jacob, and, therefore, was entitled to his father's blessing; Jacob pretended that he was Esau—he dressed like Esau, and he tried to talk like him. His old father, Isaac, was blind, and he was not quite sure that he was talking to Esau. He said: "Your voice sounds like Jacob's; come near till I touch you." Finally, the old man thought that he was talking to Esau, so he gave his blessing.

No sooner had Jacob left the room than Esau came
in, and the old father discovered his mistake!

Esau was very deeply grieved; he wept bitterly and
begged his father for a blessing also. But Isaac
had no power to take away the blessing which
he had just given to Jacob.

The old father talked very kindly to his son, but
Esau could not forgive Jacob, and made up his
mind that he would have revenge.

Just as soon as Rebekah heard what Esau was going
to do, she begged Jacob to go away from home,
and she finally contrived to have him sent to her
own old home—to his Uncle Laban.

Jacob lived with his uncle for a great many years, and
at last was married in that country so far away
from his mother. He and his Uncle Laban began
to have a little trouble, and he decided that he
would return to his old home. He ran away
secretly and took all of his family with him. But
he had no sooner gone than he began to think
it might not be safe to meet Esau. He scarcely
knew what to do, but decided to send messengers
to find out how Esau felt toward him. The messengers soon returned and reported that Esau

and four hundred men were on their way to meet
him. This was very much of a surprise to Jacob,
and it may have been a most unpleasant one. He
most likely thought that Esau was coming to take
vengeance.

Jacob did not lose his head when this report came to
him that Esau and four hundred men were on
their way to meet him; he just divided his people
into groups, and thought perhaps if one were
captured the other might be spared.

Then Jacob went in front of his family and met his
brother. As he drew near to Esau he bowed himself seven times to the ground before his brother,
and the most unexpected thing in the world happened to Jacob. Instead of punishing Jacob in
any way, Esau ran to him and embraced him, and
fell on his neck, and kissed him. Then as Esau
lifted up his eyes he saw the women and children, and he asked Jacob who they were. Jacob
said: "The children whom God hath graciously
given thy servant."

Then Jacob introduced his family to Esau and offered
him great presents, but Esau would not take them.
He said: "I have enough, my brother; let that

26

which thou hast be thine." And Jacob said: "Nay, I pray thee, if now I have found favor in thy sight, then receive my present at my hand; forasmuch as I have seen thy face, as one seeth the face of God, and thou wast pleased with me. Take, I pray thee, my gift that is brought to thee; because God hath dealt graciously with me, and because I have enough." And he urged him and he took it.

Jacob was more than glad to get back to his old home again, and he tried in every way to make up for the great wrong he had done Esau in his early life.

BATTLE HYMN OF THE REPUBLIC

Mine eyes have seen the glory of the coming of the
    Lord;
He is trampling out the vintage where the grapes of
    wrath are stored;
He hath loosed the fateful lightning of His terrible
    swift sword;
        His truth is marching on.

I have seen Him in the watch-fires of a hundred cir-
    cling camps;
They have builded Him an altar in the evening dews
    and damps;
I have read His righteous sentence by the dim and
    flaring lamps;
        His day is marching on.

He has sounded forth the trumpet that shall never call
    retreat;
He is sifting out the hearts of men before His judg-
    ment-seat;
Oh, be swift, my soul, to answer Him! be jubilant, my
    feet!
        Our God is marching on.

In the beauty of the lilies, Christ was born across
the sea,
With a glory in His bosom that transfigures you and
me;
As He died to make men holy, let us die to make men
free,
  While God is marching on.

—Julia Ward Howe.

ONE GRAND, SWEET SONG

My fairest child, I have no song to give you,
  No lark could sing 'neath skies so dull and gray,
But, if you will, a quiet hint I'll give you
  For ev'ry day, for ev'ry day.

Be good, sweet maid, and let who can be clever;
  Do noble things, not dream them all day long—
And so make life, death, and that vast forever,
  One grand, sweet song—one grand, sweet song.

—Charles Kingsley.

29

LET ME STAND AND CHEER

Dear Lord, in the battle that goes on through life,
  I ask but a field that is fair,
A chance that is equal with all in the strife,
  A courage to strive and to dare:
And if I should win, let it be by the code,
  With my faith and my honor held high;
And if I should lose, let me stand by the road,
  And cheer as the winners go by.

And, Lord, may the shouts be ungrudging and clear,
  A tribute that comes from the heart,
And let me not cherish a snarl and a sneer
  Or play any sniveling part;
Let me say, "There they ride, on whom laurels be-
      stowed,
  Since they played the game better than I."
Let me stand with a smile by the side of the road,
  And cheer as the winners go by.

So grant me to conquer, if conquer I can,
    By proving my worth in the fray,
But teach me to lose like a regular man,
    And not live a craven, I pray.
Let me take off my hat to the warriors who strode
    To victory splendid and high;
Yes, teach me to stand by the side of the road,
    And cheer as the winners go by.

—*Berton Braley.*

BREAD FROM HEAVEN

When Moses was leading the people of Israel to the
promised land, many times they made it very hard
for him. They were always fretting and grum-
bling and always without cause, for God was
with them, caring for them in every way. This
story found in the Bible tells how He gave them
bread from heaven.

And they took their journey from Elim, and all the
congregation of the children of Israel came unto
the wilderness of Sin, which is between Elim and
Sinai, on the fifteenth day of the second month
after their departing out of the land of Egypt.

And the whole congregation of the children of Israel
murmured against Moses and against Aaron in
the wilderness: and the children of Israel said
unto them, Would that we had died by the hand of
Jehovah in the land of Egypt, when we sat by the
fleshpots, when we did eat bread to the full; for
ye have brought us forth in this wilderness, to
kill this whole assembly with hunger.

Then said Jehovah unto Moses, Behold, I will rain
bread from heaven for you; and the people shall

go out and gather a day's portion every day that
I may prove them, whether they will walk in my
law, or not. And it shall come to pass on the
sixth day, that they shall prepare that which they
bring in, and it shall be twice as much as they
gather daily.

And Moses and Aaron said unto all the children of
Israel, At even, then ye shall know that Jehovah
hath brought you out from the land of Egypt: and
in the morning, then ye shall see the glory of Jehovah; for that He heareth your murmurings
against Jehovah: and what are we, that ye murmur against us? And Moses said, This shall be,
when Jehovah shall give you in the evening flesh
to eat, and in the morning bread to the full; for
that Jehovah heareth your murmurings which ye
murmur against Him; and what are we? your
murmurings are not against us, but against Jehovah.

And Moses said unto Aaron, Say unto all the congregation of the children of Israel, Come near unto
Jehovah; for He hath heard your murmurings.
And it came to pass as Aaron spake unto the
whole congregation of the children of Israel, that

they looked toward the wilderness, and, behold, the glory of Jehovah appeareth in a cloud. And Jehovah spake unto Moses, saying, I have heard the murmurings of the children of Israel: speak unto them, saying, At even ye shall eat flesh, and in the morning ye shall be filled with bread; and ye shall know that I am Jehovah your God.

And it came to pass at even, that the quail came up, and covered the camp: and in the morning the dew lay round about the camp. And when the dew that lay was gone up, behold, upon the face of the wilderness a small, round thing, small as the hoarfrost on the ground. And when the children of Israel saw it, they said one to another, What is it? for they knew not what it was. And Moses said unto them, It is the bread which Jehovah hath given you to eat. This is the thing which Jehovah hath commanded. Gather ye of it every man according to his eating; an omer a head according to the number of your persons, shall ye take it, every man for them that are in his tent.

And the children of Israel did so, and gathered some more, some less. And when they measured it with an omer, he that had gathered much had

nothing over, and he that gathered little had no lack; they gathered every man according to his eating. And Moses said unto them, Let no man leave of it till the morning. Notwithstanding, they hearkened not unto Moses; but some of them left of it till the morning, and it bred worms, and became foul: and Moses was wroth with them.

And they gathered it morning by morning every man according to his eating: and when the sun waxed hot, it melted. And it came to pass, that on the sixth day they gathered twice as much bread, two omers for each one: and all the rulers of the congregation came and told Moses.

And he said unto them, This is that which Jehovah hath spoken, To-morrow is a solemn rest, a holy sabbath unto Jehovah: bake that which ye will bake, and boil that which ye will boil; and all that remaineth over lay up for you to be kept until the morning. And they laid it up till the morning as Moses bade, and it did not become foul, neither was there any worm therein. And Moses said, Eat that to-day; for to-day is a sabbath unto Jehovah: to-day we shall not find it in the field. Six days ye shall gather it; but on the seventh day is the sabbath, in it there shall be none.

And it came to pass on the seventh day, that there went out some of the people to gather, and they found none. And Jehovah said unto Moses, How long refuse ye to keep my commandments and my laws? See, for that Jehovah hath given you the sabbath, therefore, He giveth you on the sixth day the bread of two days; abide ye every man in his place, let no man go out of the place on the seventh day. So the people rested on the seventh day.

And the house of Israel called the name thereof Manna: and it was like coriander seed, white; and the taste of it was like wafers made with honey.

And Moses said, This is the thing which Jehovah hath commanded, Let an omerful of it be kept throughout your generations, that they may see the bread wherewith I fed you in the wilderness when I brought you forth from the land of Egypt.

And Moses said unto Aaron, Take a pot, and put an omerful of manna therein, and lay it up before Jehovah, to be kept throughout your generations.

As Jehovah commanded Moses, so Aaron laid it up

before the Testimony, to be kept. And the children did eat manna forty years, until they came to a land inhabited; they did eat the manna until they came unto the borders of the land of Canaan.

—Exodus 16.

NOW THE DAY IS OVER

Sabine Baring-Gould.

Joseph Barnby.

1. Now the day is o - ver, Night is draw - ing nigh;
2. Je - sus, give the wea - ry Calm and sweet re - pose;
3. Thro' the long night-watch - es May Thine an - gels spread
4. When the morn - ing wak - ens, Then may I a - rise,

Shad - ows of the ev - 'ning Steal a - cross the sky.
With Thy ten - d'rest bless - ing May our eye - lids close.
Their white wings a - bove me, Watch - ing 'round my bed.
Pure, and fresh, and sin - less, In Thy ho - ly eyes.

ev - 'ning Steal a - cross

MOSES' CHALLENGE TO HIS PEOPLE

And Moses went and spake these words unto all Israel.

And he said unto them, I am a hundred and twenty years old this day; and I can no more go out and come in: and Jehovah hath said unto me, Thou shalt not go over this Jordan.

Jehovah thy God, He will go over before thee; He will destroy these nations from before thee, and thou shalt dispossess them: and Joshua, he shall go over before thee, as Jehovah hath spoken.

And Jehovah will do unto them as He did to Sihon and to Og, the kings of the Amorites, and unto their land; whom He destroyed.

And Jehovah will deliver them up before you, and ye shall do unto them according unto all the commandment which I have commanded you.

Be strong and of good courage, fear not, nor be affrighted at them: for Jehovah thy God He it is that doth go with thee; He will not fail thee nor forsake thee.

And Moses called unto Joshua, and said unto him in the sight of all Israel, Be strong and of good courage: for thou shalt go with this people into the land which Jehovah hath sworn unto their fathers to give them; and thou shalt cause them to inherit it.

And Jehovah, He it is that doth go before thee; He will be with thee, He will not fail thee, neither forsake thee: fear not, neither be dismayed.

—Deut. 31: 1-8.

No offerings of my own I have,
  Nor works my faith to prove;
I can but give the gifts He gave,
  And plead His love for love.

And so beside the Silent Sea
  I wait the muffled oar;
No harm from Him can come to me
  On ocean or on shore.

I know not where His islands lift
  Their fronded palms in air;
I only know I can not drift
  Beyond His love and care.

—From Whittier's "The Eternal Goodness."

MOSES' FAREWELL

Give ear, ye heavens, and I will speak;
And let the earth hear the words of my mouth.

My doctrine shall drop as the rain;
My speech shall distil as the dew,
As the small rain upon the tender grass,
And as the showers upon the herb.

For I will proclaim the name of Jehovah:
Ascribe ye greatness unto our God.

The Rock, His work is perfect;
For all His ways are justice:
A God of faithfulness and without iniquity,
Just and right is He.

They have dealt corruptly with Him, they are not His
        children, it is their blemish;
They are a perverse and crooked generation.

Do ye thus requite Jehovah,
O foolish people and unwise?

Is not He thy Father that hath bought thee?
He hath made thee, and established thee.

Remember the days of old,
Consider the years of many generations:
Ask thy Father and He will show thee;
Thine elders, and they will tell thee.

When the Most High gave to the nations their in-
    heritance,
When He separated the children of men,
He set the bounds of the peoples
According to the number of the children of Israel.

For Jehovah's portion is His people;
Jacob is the lot of His inheritance.

He found him in a desert land,
And in the waste howling wilderness;
He compassed him about, He cared for him,
He kept him as the apple of His eye.

As an eagle that stirreth up her nest,
That fluttereth over her young,

He spread abroad His wings, He took them,
He bare them on His pinions.

Jehovah alone did lead him,
And there was no foreign god with him.

He made him ride on the high places of the earth,
And he did eat the increase of the field;
And He made him to suck honey out of the rock,
And oil out of the flinty rock;

Butter of the herd, and milk of the flock,
With fat of lambs,
And rams of the breed of Bashan, and goats
With the finest of the wheat;
And of the blood of the grape thou drankest wine.

.   .   .   .

And Moses made an end of speaking all these words
    to all Israel;
And he said unto them, Set your heart unto all the
    words which I testify unto you this day, which
    ye shall command your children to observe to do,
    even all the words of this law.

For it is no vain thing for you; because it is your life, and through this thing ye shall prolong your days in the land, whither ye go over the Jordan to possess it.

And Jehovah spake unto Moses that selfsame day, saying,

Get thee up into this mountain of Abarim, unto mount Nebo, which is in the land of Moab, that is over against Jericho; and behold the land of Canaan, which I give unto the children of Israel for a possession;

And die in the mount whither thou goest up, and be gathered unto thy people, as Aaron thy brother died in mount Hor, and was gathered unto his people:

Because ye trespassed against Me in the midst of the children of Israel at the waters of Meribah of Kadesh, in the wilderness of Zin; because ye sanctified Me not in the midst of the children of Israel.

For thou shalt see the land before thee; but thou shalt not go thither into the land which I give the children of Israel.

—Deut. 32: 1-14, 45-52.

45

HOW A HAILSTORM SAVED AN ARMY

There was much work for Joshua to do after he had
become the leader of the people of Israel, for these
people were always forgetful of God's goodness
to them, and continuously doing things which
they had been forbidden to do. And many times
Joshua had to plead with them, and many times
he had to reprove them.

Joshua himself had a very hard time, for his real
work was to lead the Israelites through some
parts of the land that were inhabited by very
strong, warlike peoples, and these must all be
overcome before his people could have any peace
in their promised land.

The kings on the east side of the river Jordan had
been overcome, and stories of the great power
of the people of Israel had reached the nations
on the west side of the river, where Joshua and
his people were going. This west side of the
river was the land of Canaan, the land which had
been promised to them by Jehovah.

And now Joshua and all his followers were nearly
home; near to the home which many, many years
before had been given to their old grandfather,
Abraham.

The walls of Jericho had already fallen, and the people of the great city, Gibeon, made peace with
Joshua, because they did not want their city to
be attacked, and, somehow, they felt sure that if
it were they would all be destroyed.

After all the mighty men of Gibeon had joined themselves to Joshua, King Adonizedek, who was
reigning then in Jerusalem, was very uneasy.
He thought if he could make a league with four
other kings around him, that they would be able
to overcome the people of Israel. So the five
kings of the Amorites—Adonizedek, of Jerusalem; Hoham, king of Hebron; Piram, king of
Jarmuth; Japhia, king of Lachish, and Debir,
king of Eglon—banded themselves together to
overcome Joshua and the people of Israel.

These kings and their soldiers marched up against
Gibeon and made war against it. The men of
Gibeon immediately sent word to Joshua's camp
at Gilgal and asked him to make haste and come

up to them; they pleaded with him to come quickly: "For," said they, "all the kings of the Amorites that dwell in the hill country are gathered together against us."

Joshua and all the men of war started immediately from Gilgal, and God spoke to Joshua, saying: "Fear thou not; for I have delivered them into thy hands; there shall not a man of them stand before thee."

All night long the men marched on the way to Gibeon, and very suddenly they came upon the five kings with their great armies. God caused great confusion to come upon the kings and their armies, and Joshua and his men chased many of them away and killed many others. And as the armies ran away from the Israelites, God cast down great hailstones from heaven, and they died. The Bible says: "They were more who died with the hailstones than they whom the children of Israel slew with the sword."

It was at this great siege between Joshua and the Amorites that Joshua commanded the sun and moon to stand still. He stood before the people of Israel and called to the great sun in the heavens:

"Sun, stand thou still upon Gibeon;
And thou, moon, in the valley of Aijalon.
And the sun stood still, and the moon stayed,
Until the nation had avenged themselves of their
enemies."

And that was the only day in the world that the sun
stayed in the heavens for a longer time than
usual; and that day it stayed for hours, because
God Himself was with Joshua and all Israel.

A very strange fate befell the five kings who had taken
their men to fight Joshua and the Gibeonites; they
were hurrying as fast as they could to get away
from the fight, and they came to the cave at Mak-
kedah. They rushed into the cave and hid themselves, but some of Joshua's men found them and
came running to him with the news: "The five
kings are found hidden in the cave at Mak-
kedah."

Joshua ordered the men to stop the mouth of the cave
with great stones, and to set a few men there to
watch, but he told the others to hurry on and pur-
sue the enemy. He said: "Suffer them not to
enter into their cities, for Jehovah your God hath
delivered them into your hand."

51

Joshua's men followed until all the enemy were slain; then they returned to the cave where the kings had hidden. They opened the cave and the kings were brought out. As they were brought out before Joshua he called upon the men of Israel and said to the chiefs of the men that were with him: "Come near, and put your feet upon the necks of these kings." He then told the men that they should never be dismayed, for God would protect them from all their enemies in the same way. After the kings had been killed their bodies were placed in the cave and great stones were placed against the mouth of the cave.

Joshua's men took all the land, the hill country and the south, and the lowlands, and he obeyed all that God had told him; and Joshua and all his men returned to the camp at Gilgal.

KEEPSAKES

"Keep thy heart with all diligence; for out of it are the issues of life."

"Keep thy tongue from evil and thy lips from speaking guile."

"Little children, keep yourselves from idols."

"Keep the door of my lips."

"Keep thyself pure."

"If a man love Me, he will keep My words."

"Fear God and keep His commandments."

—The Bible.

THE SPACIOUS FIRMAMENT

The spacious firmament on high,
With all the blue, ethereal sky,
And spangled heavens, a shining frame,
Their great Original proclaim.
Th' unwearied sun, from day to day,
Does his Creator's power display,
And publishes to every land
The work of an Almighty Hand.

Soon as the evening shades prevail,
The moon takes up the wondrous tale,
And nightly, to the listening earth,
Repeats the story of her birth;
While all the stars that round her burn,
And all the planets in their turn,
Confirm the tidings as they roll,
And spread the truth from pole to pole.

What though in solemn silence all
Move round this dark, terrestrial ball—
What though no real voice nor sound
Amid their radiant orbs be found—
In reason's ear they all rejoice,
And utter forth a glorious voice;
Forever singing as they shine,
"The Hand that made us is divine."

—Joseph Addison.

THE TEN COMMANDMENTS

Thou shalt have no other gods before me.

Thou shalt not make unto thee a graven image, nor
any likeness of anything that is in heaven above,
or that is in the earth beneath, or that is in the
water under the earth: thou shalt not bow down
thyself unto them, nor serve them; for I Jehovah thy God am a jealous God, visiting the iniquity of the fathers upon the children, upon the
third and upon the fourth generations of them
that hate me, and showing lovingkindness unto
thousands of them that love me and keep my commandments.

Thou shalt not take the name of Jehovah thy God in
vain; for Jehovah will not hold him guiltless that
taketh His name in vain.

Remember the sabbath day, to keep it holy. Six days
shalt thou labor, and do all thy work; but the
seventh day is a sabbath unto Jehovah thy God:
in it thou shalt not do any work, thou, nor thy

son, nor thy daughter, thy man-servant, nor thy
maid-servant, nor thy cattle, nor thy stranger
that is within thy gates: for in six days Jehovah
made heaven and earth, the sea, and all that in
them is, and rested the seventh day; wherefore
Jehovah blessed the sabbath day, and hallowed it.

Honor thy father and thy mother, that thy days may
be long in the land which Jehovah thy God giveth
thee.

Thou shalt not kill.

Thou shalt not commit adultery.

Thou shalt not steal.

Thou shalt not bear false witness against thy neighbor.

Thou shalt not covet thy neighbor's house, thou shalt
not covet thy neighbor's wife, nor his man-servant, nor his maid-servant, nor his ox, nor his
ass, nor anything that is thy neighbor's.

GOD'S MIRACLES

To throw all the sunset colors—silver and crimson
and flame—
Over the sky each evening, yet never make them the
same.

To slip back the gates of dawning, to guide the sun
as it goes;
To sweeten the crystal snowflakes, and brighten the
cheeks of a rose.

To bring out the stars with darkness, and make a
path for the moon;
Give scent to the flower blossoms, wind-songs a wan-
dering tune.

The grass turns green when the spring comes by, the
flowers know when to grow;
The rainbow follows the shining rain, and the winds
know when to blow.

All of the things that man controls, the visions that
he makes true,
Never were half so wonderful as the miracles God can
do.

—Helen Welshimer.

58

SAMUEL'S FAREWELL ADDRESS

And Samuel said unto all Israel, Behold, I have hearkened unto your voice in all that ye said unto me, and have made a king over you.

And now, behold, the king walketh before you; and I am old and grayheaded; and, behold, my sons are with you: and I have walked before you from my youth unto this day.

Here I am: witness against me before Jehovah, and before His anointed: whose ox have I taken? or whose ass have I taken? or whom have I defrauded? whom have I oppressed? or of whose hand have I taken a ransom to blind mine eyes therewith? and I will restore it you.

And they said, Thou hast not defrauded us, nor oppressed us, neither hast thou taken aught of any man's hand.

And he said unto them, Jehovah is witness against you, and His anointed is witness this day, that ye have not found aught in my hand. And they said, He is witness.

And Samuel said unto the people, It is Jehovah that appointed Moses and Aaron, and that brought your fathers up out of the land of Egypt.

Now therefore stand still, that I may plead with you before Jehovah concerning all the righteous acts of Jehovah, which He did to you and to your fathers.

When Jacob was come into Egypt, and your fathers cried unto Jehovah, then Jehovah sent Moses and Aaron, who brought forth your fathers out of Egypt, and made them to dwell in this place.

But they forgat Jehovah their God; and He sold them into the hand of Sisera, captain of the host of Hazor, and into the hand of the Philistines, and into the hand of the king of Moab; and they fought against them.

And they cried unto Jehovah, and said, We have sinned, because we have forsaken Jehovah, and have served the Baalim and the Ashtaroth: but now deliver us out of the hand of our enemies, and we will serve Thee.

And Jehovah sent Jerubbaal, and Bedan, and Jephthah, and Samuel, and delivered you out of the hand of your enemies on every side; and ye dwelt in safety.

And when ye saw that Nahash the king of the chil-

dren of Ammon came against you, ye said unto me, Nay, but a king shall reign over us; when Jehovah your God was your king.

Now therefore behold the king whom ye have chosen, and whom ye have asked for: and, behold, Jehovah hath set a king over you.

If ye will fear Jehovah, and serve Him, and hearken unto His voice, and not rebel against the commandment of Jehovah, and both ye and also the king that reigneth over you be followers of Jehovah your God, well:

But if ye will not hearken unto the voice of Jehovah, but rebel against the commandment of Jehovah, then will the hand of Jehovah be against you, as it was against your fathers.

Now therefore stand still and see this great thing which Jehovah will do before your eyes.

Is it not wheat harvest to-day? I will call unto Jehovah, that He may send thunder and rain; and ye shall know and see that your wickedness is great, which ye have done in the sight of Jehovah, in asking you a king.

So Samuel called unto Jehovah; and Jehovah sent thunder and rain that day: and all the peo-

ple greatly feared Jehovah and Samuel.
And all the people said unto Samuel, Pray for thy servants unto Jehovah thy God, that we die not; for
we have added unto all our sins this evil, to ask
us a king.

And Samuel said unto the people, Fear not: ye have
indeed done all this evil; yet turn not aside from
following Jehovah, but serve Jehovah with all
your heart:

And turn ye not aside; for then would ye go after vain
things, which cannot profit nor deliver, for they
are vain.

For Jehovah will not forsake His people for His great
name's sake, because it hath pleased Jehovah to
make you a people unto Himself.

Moreover as for me, far be it from me that I should
sin against Jehovah in ceasing to pray for you:
but I will instruct you in the good and the
right way.

Only fear Jehovah, and serve Him in truth with all
your heart; for consider how great things He
hath done for you.

But if ye shall still do wickedly, ye shall be consumed,
both ye and your king.

1 Samuel 12.

THE CAPTAIN'S DAUGHTER

We were crowded in the cabin,
  Not a soul would dare to sleep—
It was midnight on the waters,
  And a storm was on the deep.

'Tis a fearful thing in winter
  To be shattered by the blast,
And to hear the rattling trumpet
  Thunder, "Cut away the mast!"

So we shuddered there in silence—
  For the stoutest held his breath,
While the hungry sea was roaring
  And the breakers threatened death.

And as thus we sat in darkness,
  Each one busy with his prayers,
"We are lost!" the captain shouted
  As he staggered down the stairs.

But his little daughter whispered,
  As she took his icy hand,
"Isn't God upon the ocean,
  Just the same as on the land?"

Then we kissed the little maiden,
  And we spoke in better cheer,
And we anchored safe in harbor
  When the morn was shining clear.

—*James T. Fields*.

THE CHAMBERED NAUTILUS

This is the ship of pearl which, poets feign,
    Sails the unshadowed main—
    The venturous bark that flings
On the sweet summer wind its purpled wings
In gulfs enchanted, where the Siren sings,
    And coral reefs lie bare,
Where the cold seamaids rise to sun their streaming
    hair.

Its web of living gauze no more unfurl;
    Wrecked is the ship of pearl!
    And every chambered cell,
Where its dim, dreaming life was wont to dwell,
As the frail tenant shaped his growing shell,
    Before thee lies revealed—
Its irised ceiling rent, its sunless crypt unsealed!

65

Year after year beheld the silent toil
        That spread his lustrous coil;
        Still, as the spiral grew,
He left the past year's dwelling for the new,
Stole with soft step its shining archway through,
        Built up its idle door,
Stretched in his last-found home, and knew the old no
    more.

Thanks for the heavenly message brought by thee,
        Child of the wandering sea,
        Cast from her lap, forlorn!
From thy dead lips, a clearer note is born
Than ever Triton blew from wreathed horn!
        While on my ear it rings,
Through the deep caves of thought I hear a voice that
    sings:

Build thee more stately mansions, O my soul,
        As the swift seasons roll!
        Leave thy low-vaulted past!
Let each new temple, nobler than the last,
Shut thee from heaven with a dome more vast,
        Till thou at length art free,
Leaving thine outgrown shell by life's unresting sea!

—Oliver Wendell Holmes.

THE FAILURE OF A VAIN MAN

About three thousand years ago the great King David lived. He ruled the Hebrew people, and his palace was in Jerusalem.

Among his children was a favorite son whose name was Absalom. Absalom was a very handsome young man; he was of faultless form, and had very long, fine hair, of which he was extremely vain.

Absalom caused the death of one of his half-brothers, and his old father sent him away from the palace for five years; three of these years were spent with his mother's relatives in Geshur, and the other two in Jerusalem.

It was not long after Absalom had returned to the palace that he decided to make himself king in his father's place. He planned to win the hearts of the people from King David, and he felt sure this would be the best way to gain hold on them. He had been away from the palace so long, and he had been used to the power and luxuries which a young prince receives, and he was more than anxious to regain it all; yea, even more, he was

determined to become the king, and, in order to
do this, he began to scheme for popularity.

Absalom began by deceiving the people and leading
them to believe that whatever he said was just
right. He stationed himself at the gate where
the people came and went, and never missed
an opportunity to chat with them and to make
them feel that he was deeply interested in everything that concerned them. If any man had a
complaint to take to the king, Absalom would
coax the man to tell him about it, then he would
tell the man that his claims were all right, and
would add, "Oh that I were made judge in the
land and I would do you justice!" And day after
day Absalom stole the hearts of the men of Israel
away from his old father.

Absalom went on in this way for a good many years,
until at last he had things all shaped to come out
in open rebellion against his father and take the
kingdom away from him.

When King David heard of this he prepared to leave
Jerusalem rather than be shut up and compelled
to surrender. He thought if he could only get
across the Jordan River he might have some way

of protecting himself against Absalom. He hastily crossed it, and then sent Zadok and two or three trusty men to find out what Absalom was planning to do. He also sent one servant whose name was Hushai, whom he told to join himself to Absalom's army in order to keep Zadok advised of Absalom's intentions.

Hushai proved a very good spy for David, and through Zadok gave David all the information he could gather.

Absalom in the meantime was increasing his army and preparing to send his father down in the deepest defeat.

In order to offset this move of Absalom, David was obliged to get his armies into line, though he was grieved very much to do so, and finally when the time came David reviewed the troops which were to fight for him; he went and stood by the gateway, and when he saw the hundreds and thousands of men that were passing he said to the leaders: "Deal gently with the young man Absalom for my sake." It seemed that it well-nigh broke his old heart to think of the favorite son Absalom, whose vanity had proved too much for

him. And the people as they listened to the old
man saying, "Deal gently with Absalom for my
sake," knew that the kindest-hearted king in
the world was their old King David.
Absalom's fate did not rest with King David, as may
be seen by reading of the next story, which is
taken from the Bible.

DEATH OF ABSALOM

And David numbered the people that were with him, and set captains of thousands and captains of hundreds over them. And David sent forth the people, a third part under the hand of Joab, and a third part under the hand of Abishai, the son of Zeruiah, Joab's brother, and a third part under the hand of Ittai the Gittite.

And the king said unto the people, I will surely go forth with you myself also. But the people said, Thou shalt not go forth: for if we flee away, they will not care for us; neither if half of us die, will they care for us: but thou art worth ten thousand of us; therefore now it is better that thou be ready to succor us out of the city. And the king said unto them, What seemeth you best I will do.

And the king stood by the gate-side, and all the people went out by hundreds and by thousands. And the king commanded Joab and Abishai and Ittai, saying, Deal gently for my sake with the young man, even with Absalom. And all the people heard when the king gave all the captains charge concerning Absalom.

So the people went out into the field against Israel: and the battle was in the forest of Ephraim. And the people of Israel were smitten there before the servants of David, and there was a great slaughter there that day of twenty thousand men. For the battle was there spread over the face of all the country; and the forest devoured more people that day than the sword devoured.

And Absalom chanced to meet the servants of David. And Absalom was riding upon his mule, and the mule went under the thick boughs of a great oak, and his head caught hold of the oak, and he was taken up between heaven and earth; and the mule that was under him went on.

And a certain man saw it, and told Joab, and said, Behold, I saw Absalom hanging in an oak. And Joab said unto the man that told him, And, behold, thou sawest it, and why didst thou not smite him there to the ground? And I would have given thee ten pieces of silver, and a girdle. And the man said unto Joab, Though I should receive a thousand pieces of silver in my hand, yet would I not put forth my hand against the king's son: for in our hearing the king charged thee and Abishai and Ittai, saying, Beware that none touch the young man Absalom. Otherwise if I had dealt falsely against his life (and there is no matter hid from the king), then thou thyself wouldst have set thyself against me.

Then said Joab, I may not tarry thus with thee. And he took three darts in his hand, and thrust them through the heart of Absalom, while he was yet alive in the midst of the oak. And ten young men that bare Joab's armor compassed about and smote Absalom, and slew him. And Joab blew the trumpet, and the people returned from pursuing after Israel; for Joab held back the people.

And they took Absalom, and cast him into the great pit in the forest, and raised over him a very great heap of stones: and all Israel fled every one to his tent. Now Absalom in his lifetime had taken and reared up for himself the pillar, which is in the king's dale: for he said, I have no son to keep my name in remembrance: and he called the pillar after his own name; and it is called Absalom's monument unto this day.

Then said Ahimaaz the son of Zadok, Let me now run, and bear the king tidings, how that Jehovah hath avenged him of his enemies. And Joab said unto him, Thou shalt not be the bearer of tidings this day, but thou shalt bear tidings another day, but this day thou shalt bear no tidings, because the king's son is dead. Then said Joab to the Cushite, Go, tell the king what thou hast seen. And the Cushite bowed himself unto Joab, and ran.

Then said Ahimaaz the son of Zadok yet again to Joab, But come what may, let me, I pray thee, also run after the Cushite. And Joab said, Wherefore wilt thou run, my son, seeing that thou wilt have no reward for the tidings? But come what may, said he, I will run. And he said unto him, Run. Then Ahimaaz ran by way of the Plain, and outran the Cushite.

Now David was sitting between the two gates: and the watchman went up to the roof of the gate unto the wall, and lifted up his eyes, and looked, and, behold, a man running alone. And the watchman cried, and told the king. And the king said, If he be alone, there is tidings in his mouth. And he came apace, and drew near.

And the watchman saw another man running; and the watchman called unto the porter, and said, Behold, another man running alone. And the king said, He also bringeth tidings. And the watchman said, I think the running of the foremost is like the running of Ahimaaz the son of Zadok. And the king said, He is a good man, and cometh with good tidings.

And Ahimaaz called, and said unto the king, All is well. And he bowed himself before the king with his face to the earth, and said, Blessed be Jehovah thy God, who hath delivered up the men that lifted up their hand against my lord the king. And the king said, Is it well with the young man Absalom? And Ahimaaz answered, When Joab sent the king's servant, even me thy servant, I saw a great tumult, but I knew not what it was. And the king said, Turn aside, and stand here. And he turned aside, and stood still.

And, behold, the Cushite came; and the Cushite said, Tidings for my lord the king; for Jehovah hath avenged thee this day of all them that rose up against thee. And the king said unto the

76

Cushite, Is it well with the young man Absalom? And the Cushite answered, The enemies of my lord the king, and all that rise up against thee to do thee hurt, be as that young man is. And the king was much moved, and went up to the chamber over the gate, and wept: and as he went, thus he said, O my son Absalom, my son, my son Absalom! would I had died for thee, O Absalom, my son, my son!

—2 Samuel 18.

THE CHAMBER OVER THE GATE

Is it so far from thee
Thou canst no longer see
The chamber over the gate,
That old man desolate,
Weeping and wailing sore
For his son, who is no more?
O Absalom, my son!

Is it so long ago
That cry of human woe
From the walled city came,
Calling on his dear name,
That it has died away
In the distance of to-day?
O Absalom, my son!

There is no far or near,
There is neither there nor here,
There is neither soon nor late,
In that chamber over the gate,
Nor any long ago
To that cry of human woe,
O Absalom, my son!

From the ages that are past
The voice sounds like a blast,
Over seas that wreck and drown,
Over tumult of traffic and town;
And from ages yet to be
Come the echoes back to me,
O Absalom, my son!

Somewhere at every hour
The watchman on the tower
Looks forth, and sees the fleet
Approach of hurrying feet
Of messengers, that bear
The tidings of despair.
O Absalom, my son!

He goes forth from the door,
Who shall return no more;
With him our joy departs;
The light goes out in our hearts;
In the chamber over the gate
We sit disconsolate.
O Absalom, my son!

That 'tis a common grief
Bringeth but slight relief;
Ours is the bitterest loss,
Ours is the heaviest cross;
And forever the cry will be
"Would God I had died for thee,
O Absalom, my son!"

—*Henry W. Longfellow.*

I WOULD BE TRUE

Harold Arnold Walters.

Joseph Yates Peek.

1. I would be true, for there are those who trust me; I would be
2. I would be friend of all—the foe, the friend-less; I would be

pure, for there are those who care; I would be strong, for
giv-ing, and for-get the gift; I would be hum-ble,

there is much to suf-fer; I would be brave, for there is
for I know my weak-ness; I would look up, and laugh, and

much to dare, I would be brave, for there is much to dare.
love, and lift, I would look up, and laugh, and love, and lift.

A WISE KING

King David had a son whose name was Solomon, and
he is often spoken of as the wisest king that ever
lived. He was not a vain man like his brother
Absalom had been; indeed, he was just the oppo-
site.

After the death of Absalom, King David lived in
Jerusalem. He was not a very old man, only
a little past seventy, but he felt like he wanted
to get the kingdom ready for the one who was
to succeed him—Solomon.

At one time David had wanted to build a great temple for God's worship, and had sent Nathan, the
great prophet, to intercede with Jehovah for him.
But God's plan had been to have David's son
build the temple, and the old man was very con-
tent to have it so. He began to save gold and
silver and wealth of all kinds for use in building, and he had carefully taken care of all that
would be of any service to Solomon in the building of the temple.

There had been a little trouble before Solomon was
anointed king, and it arose because he really had

an older brother who was heir to the throne. This man's name was Adonijah, and perhaps the reason he was not chosen by his father as his successor was that he was a man of "very fiery passions and haughty temperament, and would not carry out the peaceful and religious designs which David wished his successor to do."

This Adonijah made a great feast and invited many of his friends. In some way, while the feast was going on, he managed to get some one to call out, "Long live King Adonijah!" and one after another took up the cry until it seemed as if he really were the king. The good old prophet Nathan heard of this, and went right to King David and to Solomon's mother, telling them what Adonijah had done. This did not please the old king, and he immediately ordered that Solomon should be made the king. He called the priest Zadok and Nathan the prophet and another trusted officer and gave them this command:

Take with you the servants of your lord, and cause Solomon my son to ride upon mine own mule, and bring him down to Gihon:

And let Zadok the priest and Nathan the prophet

anoint him there king over Israel; and blow ye
the trumpet, and say, Long live king Solomon!
Then ye shall come up after him, and he shall come
and sit upon my throne; for he shall be king in
my stead; and I have appointed him to be prince
over Israel and over Judah.

So Zadok the priest, and Nathan the prophet, and
Benaiah the son of Jehoiada, and the Cherethites and the Pelethites, went down, and caused
Solomon to ride upon king David's mule, and
brought him to Gihon.

And Zadok the priest took the horn of oil out of the
tent, and anointed Solomon. And they blew the
trumpet; and all the people said, Long live king
Solomon!

And all the people came up after him, and the people
piped with pipes, and rejoiced with great joy, so
that the earth rent with the sound of them.

After all this Adonijah was afraid that Solomon
would kill him, and some one ran to the new king
and told him this. Solomon answered: "If he
shall show himself a worthy man, there will not a
hair of him fall to the earth." After this the
two brothers met and became good friends.

As King David grew older and he felt that he was fast leaving everything in the hands of Solomon, he said: "My son, I am going the way of all the earth: be thou strong therefore, and show thyself a man; and keep the charge of Jehovah thy God, to walk in His ways, to keep His statutes, and His commandments, and His ordinances, and His testimonies, according to that which is written in the law of Moses, that thou mayest prosper in all that thou doest, and whithersoever thou turnest thyself; that Jehovah may establish His word which He spake concerning me, saying, If thy children take heed to their way, to walk before Me in truth with all their heart and with all their soul, there shall not fail thee [said He] a man on the throne of Israel."

In the early days of his kingship Solomon learned to trust everything to Jehovah. Six miles northwest of Jerusalem, where the king's palace was situated, there is a conspicuous mountain called Gibeon. It was there that the tabernacle for God's worship had been placed, and it was to this mount that Solomon went to worship and to offer burnt-offerings upon the altar.

And the king went to Gibeon to sacrifice there; for
that was the great high place: a thousand burnt-
offerings did Solomon offer upon that altar.

In Gibeon Jehovah appeared to Solomon in a dream
by night; and God said, Ask what I shall give
thee.

And Solomon said, Thou hast showed unto Thy servant David my father great lovingkindness, according as he walked before Thee in truth, and
in righteousness, and in uprightness of heart
with Thee; and Thou hast kept for him this great
lovingkindness, that Thou hast given him a son
to sit on his throne, as it is this day.

And now, O Jehovah, my God, Thou hast made Thy
servant king instead of David my father: and I
am but a little child; I know not how to go out
or come in.

And Thy servant is in the midst of Thy people which
Thou hast chosen, a great people, that cannot be
numbered nor counted for multitude.

Give Thy servant therefore an understanding heart
to judge Thy people, that I may discern between
good and evil; for who is able to judge this Thy
great people?

And the speech pleased the Lord, that Solomon had asked this thing.

And God said unto him, Because thou hast asked this thing, and hast not asked for thyself long life, neither hast asked riches for thyself, nor hast asked the life of thine enemies, but hast asked for thyself understanding to discern justice;

Behold, I have done according to thy word: lo, I have given thee a wise and an understanding heart: so that there hath been none like thee before thee, neither after thee shall any arise like unto thee.

And I have also given thee that which thou hast not asked, both riches and honor, so that there shall not be any among the kings like unto thee, all thy days.

And if thou wilt walk in my ways, to keep my statutes and my commandments, as thy father David did walk, then I will lengthen thy days.

And Solomon awoke; and, behold, it was a dream: and he came to Jerusalem, and stood before the ark of the covenant of Jehovah, and offered up burnt-offerings, and offered peace-offerings, and made a feast to all his servants.

GO, WHEN THE MORNING SHINETH

Go, when the morning shineth,
 Go, when the moon is bright,
Go, when the eve declineth,
 Go, in the hush of night;
Go, with pure mind and feeling,
 Fling earthly thoughts away,
And in thy chamber kneeling,
 Do thou in secret pray.

Remember all who love thee,
 All who are loved by thee;
Pray for those who hate thee,
 If any such there be;
Then for thyself, in meekness,
 A blessing humbly claim,
And link with each petition
 Thy great Redeemer's name.

SOLOMON'S TEMPLE

One day when King David was sitting in his palace
he began to think about the precious things used
in God's worship. Of these things the ark of the
covenant was the most precious to him and his
people. For many years this ark of the covenant had been kept in the tabernacle which King
David did not think secure enough and splen-
did enough for God's worship.

Whenever a great wish came to the king's mind, he
was sure to ask the good prophet Nathan for his
opinion, and at this time he said to Nathan: "See,
now, I dwell in a house of cedar, but the ark of
God dwelleth within curtains."

Nathan understood very quickly that the king wanted
to build a temple, and he was pleased with the
thought and advised King David to go right
ahead with it. He said, "Go, do all that is in thy
heart; for Jehovah is with thee." But that very
same night God talked to Nathan and told him
that He had planned for David's son to build the
temple.

Nathan carried to David this news, together with a

very beautiful message which God sent to the king. This is part of the message: "I took thee from the sheep-cote, from following the sheep, that thou shouldst be a prince over my people, over Israel; and I have been with thee whithersoever thou wentest, and have cut off all thine enemies from before thee; and I will make thee a great name, like unto the name of the great ones that are in the earth."

There were a good many other things in the message, but the best part of all to King David was that which God said of Solomon: "I will be his father, and he shall be My son; if he commit iniquity, I will chasten him with the rod of men and with the stripes of the children of men; but My loving-kindness shall not depart from him, as I took it from Saul, whom I put away before thee. And thy house and thy kingdom shall be made sure forever before thee."

After the message was received, David went in his room to pray. It seemed that he could not be thankful enough for all God's goodness to him. He prayed for a long time, and almost every word of his prayer was thanksgiving for God's goodness. He said: "Thou art great, O Jehovah God: for there is none like Thee, neither is there any God besides Thee!"

It, perhaps, was not an easy thing for King David to give up his own way, but when he learned of the plan that God had mapped out, he just began to be as helpful as he could in carrying out the great plan. He began to collect gold and silver and to save up every treasure that he possibly could. When these were all placed together the amount was nearly two billion dollars.

Besides the gold and silver, there was so much brass and iron that it could not be computed. Then the great beams were made from cedars of Lebanon. Mt. Lebanon was away to the north of Jerusalem, and these great trees had to be cut down and formed into rafts and towed over to Joppa and then taken on to Jerusalem by land. Immense stones had to be hewn out of the hillsides, and as they were quarried they were numbered so that each would fit a certain place in the temple or wall.

The most skilled workmen that could be secured anywhere in the kingdom went to work on the building of the temple. Besides the many thousands that lived right in and around Jerusalem, there were a great many skilled laborers from Phœnicia and other foreign countries; of these there were thousands also.

The great building was located on Mt. Moriah, in Jerusalem, and it overlooked the valley of Kidron, and was near the Mount of Olives. No wonder so many workmen were required! For the top of that great mountain had to be leveled and the sides to the east and south, which were very precipitous, had to be walled from the bottom of the valley with many stones, and these had to be wedged into the rocks of the mountainsides.

Besides all the workmen we have mentioned, there were those skillful workers in gold and silver, who made the vessels for the altars; there were the most expert weavers of fine linen and cloth, who made the hangings for the temple.

It is a wonderful thing to read the entire description of the temple, of its great porch and of the courts and the different rooms, together with the ceremonies which would take place there,

and these are all written in the first Book of the Kings.

The great building was one hundred and twenty feet long, sixty feet wide and forty-five feet high. There were many beautiful terraces in the courts, and these were adorned with trees. It required these thousands and thousands of men seven and one-half years to build the temple. The workmen all wrought with hearty good will, because they were building a house for God's worship.

Those who chopped down the cedars of Lebanon, those who dug the huge stones out of the mountainsides, those who placed them together again in the walls of the temple, those who worked so splendidly on the gold and silver candlesticks and other vessels, all were happy because the great house of worship was to the Father in heaven.

It is almost impossible for us to think just how this wonderful building looked. There were those who polished and polished the great brass altar until it shone like gold, and on either side of this there were great golden candlesticks—five on the right and five on the left hand. The inner doors were made of gold, and there was nothing too fine or beautiful to be used in this wonderful building.

After it was all finished the people wanted to have a great time of rejoicing, and Solomon planned that all of the people of the whole country should be there.

The ark was put in its place and great bands of musicians, clothed in white, stood on each side of the altar. All the people stood waiting—there were thousands upon thousands of them—and their king, the good, wise Solomon, marched in. He was attended by five hundred guards; the guards wore golden shields. It was a wonderful sight. Everybody sang one of King David's hymns:

"Oh give thanks unto the Lord, for He is good:
For His lovingkindness endureth for ever."

A great cloud filled the temple, and this was Jehovah's sign to the people that He understood and accepted their thanks. Then Solomon went up to the altar and lifted his hands and prayed this beautiful prayer:

O Jehovah, the God of Israel, there is no God like Thee, in heaven above, or on earth beneath; who

keepest covenant and lovingkindness with Thy
servants, that walk before Thee with all their
heart; who hast kept with Thy servant David my
father that which Thou didst promise him: yea,
Thou spakest with Thy mouth, and hast fulfilled
it with Thy hand, as it is this day.

Now therefore, O Jehovah, the God of Israel, keep
with Thy servant David my father that which
Thou hast promised him, saying, There shall not
fail thee a man in My sight to sit on the throne
of Israel, if only thy children take heed to their
way, to walk before Me as thou hast walked
before Me.

Now therefore, O God of Israel, let Thy word, I pray
Thee, be verified, which Thou spakest unto Thy
servant David my father.

But will God in very deed dwell on the earth? behold,
heaven and the heaven of heavens cannot contain Thee; how much less this house that I have
builded!

Yet have Thou respect unto the prayer of Thy servant, and to his supplication, O Jehovah my God,
to hearken unto the cry and to the prayer which
Thy servant prayeth before Thee this day;

That Thine eyes may be open toward this house night
and day, even toward the place whereof Thou
hast said, My name shall be there; to hearken
unto the prayer which Thy servant shall pray
toward this place.

And hearken Thou to the supplication of Thy servant,
and of Thy people Israel, when they shall pray
toward this place: yea, hear Thou in heaven Thy
dwelling-place; and when Thou hearest, forgive.

—1 Kings 8: 23-30.

This is a very short part of the prayer which Solomon made on the day the temple was dedicated,
and after it was all finished he arose from before the altar with his hands spread forth toward
heaven. Then he blessed all the people who were
assembled that day. He told them to live very
close to God. He said: "Jehovah, our God, be
with us, as He was with our fathers."

After the temple was dedicated to God's worship the
people had a great feast which lasted for seven
days. On the eighth day he sent the people
away; and they went to their tents glad and
happy, blessing their king and worshiping Jehovah.

KING SOLOMON AND THE ANTS

Out from Jerusalem
   The king rode with his great
   War chiefs and lords of state,
And Sheba's queen with them;

Comely, but black withal,
   To whom, perchance, belongs
   That wondrous Song of Songs,
Sensuous and mystical,

Whereto devout souls turn
   In fond, ecstatic dream,
   And through its earth-born theme
The love of loves discern.

Proud in the Syrian sun,
   In gold and purple sheen,
   The dusky Ethiop queen
Smiled on King Solomon.

Wisest of men, he knew
   The languages of all
   The creatures great and small
That trod the earth or flew.

Across an ant-hill led
  The king's path, and he heard
  Its small folk, and their word
He thus interpreted:

"Here comes the king men greet
  As wise and good and just,
  To crush us in the dust
Under his heedless feet."

The great king bowed his head,
  And saw the wide surprise
  Of the Queen of Sheba's eyes
As he told her what they said.

"O king!" she whispered sweet,
  "Too happy fate have they
  Who perish in thy way
Beneath thy gracious feet!

"Thou of the God-lent crown,
  Shall these vile creatures dare
  Murmur against thee where
The knees of kings kneel down?"

"Nay," Solomon replied,
  "The wise and strong should seek
  The welfare of the weak,"
And turned his horse aside.

His train, with quick alarm,
  Curved with their leader round
  The ant-hill's peopled mound,
And left it free from harm.

The jeweled head bent low;
  "O king!" she said, "henceforth
  The secret of thy worth
And wisdom well I know.

"Happy must be the state
  Whose ruler heedeth more
  The murmurs of the poor
Than flatteries of the great."

—John Greenleaf Whittier.

------------------- ❖ -------------------

Whene'er a noble deed is wrought,
Whene'er is spoken a noble thought,
Our hearts in glad surprise
To higher levels rise.

—Longfellow.

WHENCE COMES THE WEATHER

Behold, God is great, and we know Him not;
The number of His years is unsearchable.
For He draweth up the drops of water,
Which distil in rain from His vapor,

Which the skies pour down,
And drop upon man abundantly.
Yea, can any understand the spreadings of the cloud,
The thunderings of His pavilion?

—Job 36: 26-30.

God thundereth marvellously with His voice;
Great things doeth He, which we cannot comprehend.
For He saith to the snow, Fall thou on the earth;
Likewise to the shower of rain,
And to the showers of His mighty rain.

Out of the chamber of the south cometh the storm,
And cold out of the north.
By the breath of God ice is given;
And the breadth of the waters is straitened.

Yea, He ladeth the thick cloud with moisture;
He spreadeth abroad the cloud of His lightning:

And it is turned round about by His guidance,
That they may do whatsoever He commandeth them
Upon the face of the habitable world,
Whether it be for correction, or for His land,
Or for lovingkindness, that He cause it to come.

Hast Thou entered the treasuries of the snow,
Or hast thou seen the treasuries of the hail,
Which I have reserved against the time of trouble,
Against the day of battle and war?
By what way is the light parted,
Or the east wind scattered upon the earth?
Who hath cleft a channel for the water flood,
Or a way for the lightning of the thunder;
To cause it to rain on a land where no man is;
On the wilderness, wherein there is no man;
To satisfy the waste and desolate ground,
And to cause the tender grass to spring forth?

Canst thou lift up thy voice to the clouds,
That abundance of waters may cover thee?
Canst thou send forth lightnings, that they may go,
And say unto thee, Here we are?
Who can number the clouds by wisdom?

Or who can pour out the bottles of heaven?
When the dust runneth into a mass,
And the clods cleave fast together?

—Job 36: 27, 28.

Who covereth the heavens with clouds,
Who prepareth rain for the earth,
Who maketh grass to grow upon the mountains.
He giveth snow like wool;
He scattereth the hoar-frost like ashes.
He casteth forth his ice like morsels:
Who can stand before His cold?
He sendeth out His word and melteth them:
He causeth His wind to blow, and the waters flow.

—Psalm 147.

When He uttereth His voice, there is tumult of waters
    in the heavens.
And He causeth the vapors to ascend from the ends of
    the earth;
He maketh lightnings for the rain, and bringeth forth
    the wind out of His treasuries.

—Jer. 10: 13.

108

ONWARD, CHRISTIAN SOLDIERS

Sabine Baring-Gould.

Arthur Sullivan.

1. Onward, Christian soldiers, Marching as to war, With the cross of Je - sus
2. At the sign of tri-umph Satan's host doth flee; On, then, Christian soldiers,
3. Like a might-y ar - my Moves the Church of God; Brothers, we are treading
4. Onward, then, ye people, Join our happy throng, Blend with ours your voices

Go - ing on be - fore! Christ, the roy-al Mas - ter, Leads a-gainst the foe;
On to vic - to - ry! Hell's foun-da-tions quiv-er At the shout of praise;
Where the saints have trod; We are not di - vid - ed; All one bod - y we,
In the tri-umph song; Glo-ry, laud, and hon - or, Un-to Christ the King;

REFRAIN.

For-ward in - to bat - tle, See, His banner go!
Brothers, lift your voices, Loud your anthems raise! Onward, Christian soldiers,
One in hope and doc-trine, One in char - i - ty.
This thro' countless a - ges Men and angels sing.

March-ing as to war, With the cross of Je - sus Go-ing on be - fore! A-MEN.

THE AMERICAN FLAG

When Freedom, from her mountain height,
  Unfurl'd her standard to the air,
She tore the azure robe of night,
  And set the stars of glory there.
She mingled with its gorgeous dyes
The milky baldric of the skies,

And striped its pure, celestial white
With streakings of the morning light;
Then, from his mansion in the sun,
She called her eagle-bearer down,
And gave into his mighty hand
The symbol of her chosen land.

Majestic monarch of the cloud!
  Who rear'st aloft thy regal form,
To hear the tempest trumpings loud,
And see the lightning-lances driven,
  When strive the warriors of the storm,
And rolls the thunder-drum of heaven;
Child of the sun! to thee 'tis given
  To guard the banner of the free,
To hover in the sulphur smoke,
To ward away the battle-stroke,
And bid its blendings shine afar,
Like rainbows in the cloud of war,
  The harbinger of victory.

Flag of the brave! thy folds shall fly
The sign of hope and triumph high.

When speaks the signal-trumpet tone,
And the long line comes gleaming on,
Ere yet the life-blood, warm and wet,
Has dimmed the glistening bayonet,
Each soldier eye shall brightly turn
To where thy meteor glories burn,
And as his springing steps advance
Catch war and vengeance from the glance;
And when the cannon-mouthings loud
Heave, in wild wreaths, the battle-shroud,
And gory sabers rise and fall,
Like shoots of flame on midnight's pall,
Then shall thy victor glances glow,
　　And cowering foes shall sink beneath
Each gallant arm, that strikes below
　　That awful messenger of death.

Flag of the seas! on ocean's wave
Thy stars shall glitter o'er the brave.
When death, careering on the gale,
Sweeps darkly round the bellied sail,
And frighted waves rush wildly back,
Before the broadside's reeling rack,

The dying wanderer of the sea
Shall look at once to heaven and thee,
And smile to see thy splendors fly
In triumph o'er his closing eye.

Flag of the free heart's only home!
 By angel hands to valor given,
Thy stars have lit the welkin dome,
 And all thy hues were born in heaven.
Forever float that standard sheet!
 Where breathes the foe but falls before us,
With Freedom's soil beneath our feet,
 And Freedom's banner waving o'er us.

      —*Joseph Rodman Drake.*

MY FLAG

They took the red from the sunset,
 The blue from the morning sky,
The white from a drift in cloudland,
 And wove them so wondrous that I
Can only stand by and cheer it,
 As it flings out its message so true:
Yes, I cheer it, and hail it as my Flag,
 The one only:—Red, White and Blue.

A CALL FOR PRAISE

Praise ye Jehovah.
Praise ye Jehovah from the heavens:
Praise Him in the heights.

Praise ye Him, all His angels:
Praise ye Him, all His host.

Praise ye Him, sun and moon:
Praise Him, all ye stars of light.

Praise Him, ye heavens of heavens,
And ye waters that are above the heavens.

Let them praise the name of Jehovah;
For He commanded, and they were created.
He hath also established them for ever and ever:
He hath made a decree which shall not pass away.

Praise Jehovah from the earth,
Ye sea-monsters, and all deeps;
Fire and hail, snow and vapor;
Stormy wind, fulfilling His word;

Mountains and all hills;
Fruitful trees and all cedars;
Beasts and all cattle;
Creeping things and flying birds;
Kings of the earth and all peoples;
Princes and all judges of the earth;
Both young men and virgins;
Old men and children:
Let them praise the name of Jehovah;
For His name alone is exalted;
His glory is above the earth and the heavens.

And He hath lifted up the horn of His people,
The praise of all His saints;
Even of the children of Israel, a people near unto Him.
Praise ye Jehovah.   —Psalm 148.

———————❖———————

Think truly, and thy thoughts
    Shall the world's famine feed;
Speak truly, and each word of thine
    Shall be a fruitful seed;
Live truly, and thy life shall be
    A great and noble creed.

—H. Bonar.

A DRINK FROM THE OLD WELL

Sometimes when one has been away from home for a
long time, he will get homesick just for the sight of
an old tree that stands in the yard there; or for
the old grapevine where he used to swing; or, it
may be, some other thing that was dear to him.

Although King David was a powerful king, he thought
many times about his old home in Bethlehem,
and he, too, would get homesick.   And sometimes
it would seem to him that he would give anything
just to be back there drinking at the old well.

David was born at Bethlehem.   Out on the hills just
south of the city, he had watched his father's
flocks.   It was there that he had practiced with
his sling, and, tiring of that, had laid it aside to
pick up the harp and sing beautiful psalms to
Jehovah.

Over at the home there was the old well, and when
David came in tired and thirsty from the field,
nothing seemed quite so good to him as a drink of
its cool, refreshing water.

Once David was away from home a long, long time;
he had grown into manhood, and King Saul was

afraid that this young man, who was so much beloved by every one, would become the king in his place; and he had made it very dangerous for David to live around there. David had gathered a group of men about him, and went to live in the wilderness. Most of the time he slept in a cave called "the cave of Adullam." He spent several years in this way, knowing that some day in God's own good time he himself would be the king in place of the wicked one from whom he was hiding.

It was while David was in exile that word came to him that the Philistines were fighting against the city of Keilah and robbing the people of their threshing-floors. As was the usual custom with David, he took the matter in prayer to God, asking for His guidance. God's message came back to him to go and smite the Philistines and save Keilah. David's men said to him: "We are afraid even here in Judah, and how much more then shall we be afraid to go against the Philistines." David again spoke to God, and this time the answer came with emphasis: "I will deliver the Philistines into thy hands."

Among the men who followed David were some of the strongest, best men in the whole country; nevertheless, the heart of the strongest would quake when orders to meet the Philistines came, for the Philistines were a race of giants.

These men all knew that when the word of God was given it was sure and stedfast. So, when David told them that they were to fight the Philistines who had come up there year after year to take the grain from the people of Keilah, they did not hesitate to follow His word.

God did just what He had promised, and the Philistines were slain. The garrison of the Philistines was in Bethlehem, and as David thought about his old home town, and the well where he used to drink, he said: "Oh that one would give me water to drink of the well of Bethlehem which is by the gate!" Just as soon as David's mighty men heard him say this three of them started out. They loved him very dearly, and they wanted their leader to have anything he asked for.

It was a dangerous thing for the men to try to break through the lines of the Philistines, but

they did not mind it, for were they not working for David, their beloved king to be? They drew the water from the well and brought it to David. When the men came back and gave the pitcher of water to David, he felt as though he could drink every drop of it, and he eagerly raised the pitcher to his lips. But quickly he stopped and lowered it again. He knew that his men had risked their very lives to get that water for him, and, while he was very happy that they should have done it, he thought to himself: "It would be just like taking the lives of these men to drink that water." And he said: "Because the men were so brave and brought me this water which would taste better than anything else to me, because it came from the old well at Bethlehem, and because it is the thing that I most want now, I will give it up as a sacrifice to God, for His loving-kindness to me." And, even though David wanted the water so much, he poured it out as a sacrifice to God, saying as he did so: "Be it far from me, O Jehovah, that I should do this. I will not drink the blood of the men that went in jeopardy of their lives."

WATCHMAN, TELL US OF THE NIGHT

John Bowring.

Lowell Mason.

1. Watch-man, tell us of the night, What its signs of prom-ise are.
2. Watch-man, tell us of the night, High - er yet the star as - cends.
3. Watch-man, tell us of the night, For the morn-ing seems to dawn.

Trav - 'ler, o'er yon mountain's height See that glo - ry-beam-ing star!
Trav - 'ler, bless - ed - ness and light, Peace and truth, its course por-tends.
Trav - 'ler, dark-ness takes its flight, Doubt and ter - ror are with-drawn.

Watch-man, does its beau-teous ray Aught of hope or joy fore-tell?
Watch-man, will its beams a - lone Gild the spot that gave them birth?
Watch-man, let thy wand'ring cease: Hie thee to thy qui - et home!

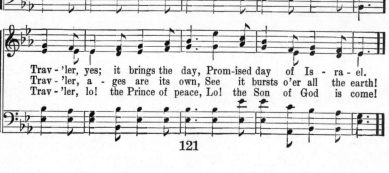

Trav - 'ler, yes; it brings the day, Prom-ised day of Is - ra - el.
Trav - 'ler, a - ges are its own, See it bursts o'er all the earth!
Trav - 'ler, lo! the Prince of peace, Lo! the Son of God is come!

121

THE SANDPIPER

Across the lonely beach we flit,
   One little sandpiper and I,
And fast I gather, bit by bit,
   The scattered driftwood, bleached and dry.
The wild waves reach their hands for it,
   The wild wind races, the tide runs high,
As up and down the beach we flit,
   One little sandpiper and I.

Above our heads the sullen clouds
  Scud, black and swift, across the sky;
Like silent ghosts in misty shrouds
  Stand out the white lighthouses high.
Almost as far as eye can reach
  I see the close-reefed vessels fly,
As fast we flit along the beach,
  One little sandpiper and I.

I watch him as he skims along,
  Uttering his sweet and mournful cry:
He starts not at my fitful song,
  Nor flash of fluttering drapery.
He has no thought of any wrong,
  He scans me with a fearless eye;
Stanch friends are we, well tried and strong,
  The little sandpiper and I.

Comrade, where wilt thou be to-night,
  When the loosed storm breaks furiously?
My driftwood fire will burn so bright!
  To what warm shelter canst thou fly?
I do not fear for thee, though wroth
  The tempest rushes through the sky;
For are we not God's children both,
  Thou, little sandpiper, and I?

—*Celia Thaxter.*

124

JESUS' BIRTH FORETOLD

The people that walked in darkness have seen a great
light: they that dwelt in the land of the shadow
of death, upon them hath the light shined.

Thou hast multiplied the nation, thou hast increased
their joy: they joy before thee according to the
joy in harvest, as men rejoice when they divide
the spoil.

For the yoke of his burden and the staff of his shoulder, the rod of His oppressor, Thou hast broken
as in the day of Midian.

For all the armor of the armed man in the tumult,
and the garments rolled in blood, shall be for
burning, for fuel of fire.

For unto us a child is born, unto us a son is given;
and the government shall be upon His shoulder:
and His name shall be called Wonderful, Coun-
sellor, Mighty God, Everlasting Father, Prince
of Peace.

—Isa. 9: 2-7.

125

WHILE SHEPHERDS WATCHED

While shepherds watched their flocks by night,
  All seated on the ground,
The Angel of the Lord came down,
  And glory shone around.

"Fear not," said he (for mighty dread
  Had seized their troubled mind);
"Glad tidings of great joy I bring
  To you and all mankind.

"To you in David's town this day
  Is born of David's line
The Saviour, who is Christ the Lord,
  And this shall be the sign:

"The heavenly Babe you there shall find
  To human view displayed,
All meanly wrapped in swathing-bands,
  And in a manger laid."

Thus spake the seraph; and forthwith
   Appeared a shining throng
Of angels praising God, and thus
   Addressed their joyful song:

"All glory be to God on high,
   And on earth be peace;
Good-will henceforth from heaven to men
   Begin, and never cease!"

                   —*Nahum Tate.*

THE GOLDEN CAROL

We saw the light shine out afar,
   On Christmas in the morning,
And straight we knew it was Christ's Star,
   Bright beaming in the morning
Then did we fall on bended knee,
   On Christmas in the morning,
And praised the Lord, who'd let us see
   His glory at its dawning.

Oh! ever thought be of His Name,
   On Christmas in the morning,
Who bore for us both grief and shame,
   Afflictions sharpest scorning.
And may we die (when death shall come)
   On Christmas in the morning,
And see in heaven our glorious home,
   The Star of Christmas morning.

—Old English.

STAR OF BETHLEHEM

When marshaled on the nightly plain,
   The glittering host bestud the sky,
One star alone, of all the train,
   Can fix the sinner's wondering eye.
Hark! hark! to God the chorus breaks,
   From every host, from every gem;
But one alone, the Saviour speaks,
   It is the star of Bethlehem.

It was my guide, my light, my all,
   It bade my dark forebodings cease,
And, through the storm and danger's thrall,
   It led me to the port of peace.
Now, safely moor'd, my perils o'er,
   I'll sing first in night's diadem,
Forever and forever more,
   The star, the star of Bethlehem.

—Henry Kirk White.

WE THREE KINGS OF ORIENT

John H. Hopkins.   John H. Hopkins.

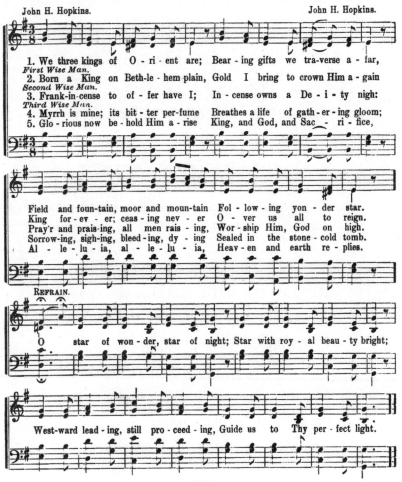

1. We three kings of O - ri - ent are; Bear - ing gifts we tra-verse a - far,
First Wise Man.
2. Born a King on Beth-le - hem plain, Gold I bring to crown Him a - gain
Second Wise Man.
3. Frank-in-cense to of - fer have I; In - cense owns a De - i - ty nigh:
Third Wise Man.
4. Myrrh is mine; its bit - ter per-fume Breathes a life of gath - er - ing gloom;
5. Glo - rious now be - hold Him a - rise King, and God, and Sac - ri - fice,

Field and foun-tain, moor and moun-tain Fol - low - ing yon - der star.
King for - ev - er; ceas - ing nev - er O - ver us all to reign.
Pray'r and prais-ing, all men rais - ing, Wor - ship Him, God on high.
Sorrow-ing, sigh-ing, bleed-ing, dy - ing Sealed in the stone - cold tomb.
Al - le - lu - ia, al - le - lu - ia, Heav - en and earth re - plies.

REFRAIN.

O star of won - der, star of night; Star with roy - al beau - ty bright;

West-ward lead - ing, still pro - ceed - ing, Guide us to Thy per - fect light.

BRIGHTEST AND BEST

Reginald Heber.

Lowell Mason.

1. Bright-est and best of the sons of the morn-ing, Dawn on our
2. Cold on His cra-dle the dew-drops are shin-ing; Low lies His
3. Say, shall we yield Him, in cost-ly de-vo-tion, O-dors of
4. Vain-ly we of-fer each am-ple ob-la-tion, Vain-ly with
5. Bright-est and best of the sons of the morn-ing, Dawn on our

dark-ness and lend us thine aid Star of the east, the ho-ri-zon a-
head with the beasts of the stall; An-gels a-dore Him, in slum-ber re-
E-dom, and off'rings di-vine, Gems of the mountain, and pearls of the
gifts would His fa-vor se-cure; Rich-er by far is the heart's ad-o-
dark-ness, and lend us thine aid; Star of the east, the ho-ri-zon a-

dorn-ing, Guide where our in-fant Re-deem-er is laid.
clin-ing, Mak-er and Mon-arch and Sav-ior of all.
o-cean, Myrrh from the for-est, and gold from the mine?
ra-tion, Dear-er to God are the pray'rs of the poor.
dorn-ing, Guide where our in-fant Re-deem-er is laid.

131

THE GOOD COMPANY PSALM

Blessed is the man that walketh not in the counsel of
    the wicked,
Nor standeth in the way of sinners,
Nor sitteth in the seat of scoffers:
But his delight is in the law of Jehovah;
And on his law doth he meditate day and night.
And he shall be like a tree planted by the streams of
    water,
That bringeth forth its fruit in its season,
Whose leaf also doth not wither;
And whatsoever he doeth shall prosper.
The wicked are not so,
But are like the chaff which the wind driveth away.
Therefore the wicked shall not stand in the judgment,
Nor sinners in the congregation of the righteous.
For Jehovah knoweth the way of the righteous;
But the way of the wicked shall perish.

—Psalm. 1.

I SHALL NOT PASS AGAIN THIS WAY

The bread that giveth strength I want to give,
The water pure that bids the thirsty live;
I want to help the fainting day by day,
I'm sure I shall not pass again this way.

I want to give the oil of joy for tears,
The faith to conquer crowding doubts and fears;
Beauty for ashes may I give alway,
I'm sure I shall not pass again this way.

I want to give good measure, running o'er,
And into angry hearts I want to pour
The answer soft that turneth wrath away;
I'm sure I shall not pass again this way.

I want to give to others hope and faith;
I want to do all that the Master saith;
I want to live aright from day to day,
I'm sure I shall not pass again this way.

—Unknown.

THE TEMPTATION

And Jesus, full of the Holy Spirit, returned from the Jordan, and was led in the Spirit in the wilderness during forty days, being tempted of the devil.

And He did eat nothing in those days: and when they were completed, He hungered.

And the devil said unto Him, If Thou art the Son of God, command this stone that it become bread.

And Jesus answered unto him, It is written, Man shall not live by bread alone.

And he led Him up, and showed Him all the kingdoms of the world in a moment of time.

And the devil said unto Him, To Thee will I give all this authority, and the glory of them: for it hath been delivered unto me; and to whomsoever I will I give it.

If Thou therefore wilt worship before me, it shall all be Thine.

And Jesus answered and said unto him, It is written, Thou shalt worship the Lord thy God, and Him only shalt thou serve.

And he led Him to Jerusalem, and set Him on the

135

pinnacle of the temple, and said unto Him, If
Thou art the Son of God, cast Thyself down
from hence:
For it is written,
He shall give His angels charge concerning Thee,
to guard Thee:
And,
On their hands they shall bear Thee up,
Lest haply Thou dash Thy foot against a stone.
And Jesus answering said unto him, It is said, Thou
shalt not make trial of the Lord thy God.
And when the devil had completed every temptation,
he departed from Him for a season.

—Luke 4: 1-13.

LOOK UNTO HEAVEN

Look unto heaven!
The still and solemn stars are burning there,
Like altars lighted in the upper air,
And to the worship of the great God given,
Where the pure spirits of the unsinning dead,
Redeemed and sanctified from earth, might shed
The holiness of prayer.

136

Look ye above!
The earth is glorious with its summer wreath;
The tall trees bend with verdure; and, beneath,
Young flowers are blushing like unwhispered love.
Yet these will change—Earth's glories be no more,
And all her bloom and greenness fade before
          The ministry of Death.

          Then, gaze not there.
God's constant miracle—the star-wrought sky—
Bends o'er ye, lifting silently on high,
As with an Angel's hand, the soul of prayer;
And Heaven's own language to the pure of Earth,
Written in stars at Nature's mighty birth,
          Burns on the gazing eye.

          Oh! turn ye, then,
And bend the knee of worship; and the eyes
Of the pure stars shall smile, with glad surprise,
At the deep reverence of the sons of men.
Oh! bend in worship, till those stars grow dim,
And the skies vanish, at the thought of Him
          Whose light beyond them lies!

—*John Greenleaf Whittier.*

JESUS HELPING OTHERS

And a certain centurion's servant, who was dear unto him, was sick and at the point of death.

And when he heard concerning Jesus, he sent unto Him elders of the Jews, asking Him that He would come and save his servant.

And they, when they came to Jesus, besought Him earnestly, saying, He is worthy that Thou shouldest do this for him; for he loveth our nation, and himself built us our synagogue.

And Jesus went with them. And when He was now not far from the house, the centurion sent friends to Him, saying unto Him, Lord, trouble not Thyself; for I am not worthy that Thou shouldest come under my roof:

Wherefore neither thought I myself worthy to come unto Thee: but say the word, and my servant shall be healed.

For I also am a man set under authority, having under myself soldiers: and I say to this one, Go, and he goeth; and to another, Come, and he cometh; and to my servant, Do this, and he doeth it.

And when Jesus heard these things, He marvelled at him, and turned and said unto the multitude that followed Him, I say unto you, I have not found so great faith, no, not in Israel.

And they that were sent, returning to the house, found the servant whole.

And it came to pass soon afterwards, that He went to a city called Nain; and His disciples went with Him, and a great multitude.

Now when He drew near to the gate of the city, behold, there was carried out one that was dead, the only son of his mother, and she was a widow: and much people of the city was with her.

And when the Lord saw her, He had compassion on her, and said unto her, Weep not.

And He came nigh and touched the bier: and the bearers stood still. And He said, Young man, I say unto thee, Arise.

And he that was dead sat up, and began to speak. And He gave him to his mother.

And fear took hold on all: and they glorified God, saying, A great prophet is arisen among us: and, God hath visited His people.

—Luke 7: 2-16.

JESUS WALKS ON THE WATER

And straightway He constrained the disciples to enter
into the boat, and to go before Him unto the
other side, till He should send the multitudes
away.

And after He had sent the multitudes away, He went
up into the mountain apart to pray: and when
even was come, He was there alone.

But the boat was now in the midst of the sea, dis-
tressed by the waves; for the wind was con-
trary.

And in the fourth watch of the night He came unto
them, walking upon the sea.

And when the disciples saw Him walking on the sea,
they were troubled, saying, It is a ghost; and
they cried out for fear.

But straightway Jesus spake unto them, saying, Be of
good cheer; it is I; be not afraid.

And Peter answered Him and said, Lord, if it be Thou,
bid me come unto Thee upon the waters.

And He said, Come. And Peter went down from the
boat, and walked upon the waters to come to
Jesus.

But when he saw the wind, he was afraid; and beginning to sink, he cried out, saying, Lord, save me.

And immediately Jesus stretched forth His hand, and took hold of him, and saith unto him, O thou of little faith, wherefore didst thou doubt?

And when they were gone up into the boat, the wind ceased.

And they that were in the boat worshipped Him, saying, Of a truth Thou art the Son of God.

And when they had crossed over, they came to the land, unto Gennesaret.

And when the men of that place knew Him, they sent into all the region round about, and brought unto Him all that were sick;

And they besought Him that they might only touch the border of His garment: and as many as touched were made whole.

—Matt. 14: 22-36.

143

THE TRANSFIGURATION

And it came to pass about eight days after these say-
ings, that He took with Him Peter and John and
James, and went up into the mountain to pray.

And as He was praying, the fashion of His countenance was altered, and His raiment become white
and dazzling.

And behold, there talked with Him two men, who
were Moses and Elijah;

Who appeared in glory, and spake of His decease
which He was about to accomplish at Jerusalem.

Now Peter and they that were with Him were heavy
with sleep: but when they were fully awake, they
saw His glory, and the two men that stood with
Him.

And it came to pass, as they were parting from Him,
Peter said unto Jesus, Master, it is good for us to
be here: and let us make three tabernacles; one
for Thee, and one for Moses, and one for Elijah:
not knowing what he said.

And while he said these things, there came a cloud,
and overshadowed them: and they feared as they
entered into the cloud.

145

And a Voice came out of the cloud, saying, This is My
 Son, My chosen: hear ye Him.
And when the Voice came, Jesus was found alone.
And they held their peace, and told no man in those
 days any of the things which they had seen.

—Luke 9:28-36.

HUMILITY

The bird that soars on highest wing
 Builds on the ground her lowly nest;
And she that doth most sweetly sing,
 Sits in the shade when all things rest.
The saint that wears heaven's brightest crown,
 In deepest adoration bends;
The weight of glory bows him down,
 Then most, when most his soul ascends;
Nearest the throne itself must be
 The footstool of humility.

—James Montgomery.

SOME STORIES JESUS TOLD

THE GOOD SAMARITAN.

And behold, a certain lawyer stood up and made trial of Him, saying, Teacher, what shall I do to inherit eternal life?

And he said unto him, What is written in the law? how readest thou?

And he answering said, Thou shalt love the Lord thy God with all thy heart, and with all thy soul, and with all thy strength, and with all thy mind; and thy neighbor as thyself.

And He said unto him, Thou hast answered right: this do, and thou shalt live.

But he, desiring to justify himself, said unto Jesus, And who is my neighbor?

Jesus made answer and said, A certain man was going down from Jerusalem to Jericho; and he fell among robbers, who both stripped him and beat him, and departed, leaving him half dead.

And by chance a certain priest was going down that way: and when he saw him, he passed by on the other side.

And in like manner a Levite also, when he came to
the place, and saw him, passed by on the other
side.

But a certain Samaritan, as he journeyed, came
where he was: and when he saw him, he was
moved with compassion,

And came to him, and bound up his wounds, pouring
on them oil and wine; and he set him on his own
beast, and brought him to an inn, and took care
of him.

And on the morrow he took out two shillings, and gave
them to the host, and said, Take care of him; and
whatsoever thou spendest more, I, when I come
back again, will repay thee.

Which of these three, thinkest thou, proved neighbor
unto him that fell among the robbers?

And he said, He that showed mercy on him.   And
Jesus said unto him, Go, and do thou likewise.

—Luke 10: 25-37.

THE PRODIGAL SON.

And He said, A certain man had two sons:

And the younger of them said to his father, Father,
give me the portion of thy substance that falleth
to me.   And he divided unto them his living.

And not many days after, the younger son gathered
all together and took his journey into a far country; and there he wasted his substance with
riotous living.

And when he had spent all, there arose a mighty
famine in that country; and he began to be in
want.

And he went and joined himself to one of the citizens
of that country; and he sent him into his fields
to feed swine.

And he would fain have filled his belly with the husks
that the swine did eat: and no man gave unto
him.

But when he came to himself he said, How many hired
servants of my father's have bread enough and
to spare, and I perish here with hunger!

I will arise and go to my father, and will say unto
him, Father, I have sinned against heaven, and
in thy sight: I am no more worthy to be called
thy son: make me as one of thy hired servants.

And he arose, and came to his father. But while
he was yet afar off, his father saw him, and was
moved with compassion, and ran, and fell on his
neck, and kissed him.

151

And the son said unto him, Father, I have sinned
against heaven, and in thy sight: I am no more
worthy to be called thy son.

But the father said to his servants, Bring forth
quickly the best robe, and put it on him; and put
a ring on his hand and shoes on his feet:

And bring the fatted calf, and kill it, and let us eat,
and make merry:

For this my son was dead, and is alive again; he was
lost, and is found.   And they began to be merry.

Now his elder son was in the field: and as he came
and drew nigh to the house, he heard music and
dancing.   And he called to him one of the servants, and inquired what these things might be.

And he said unto him, Thy brother is come; and thy
father hath killed the fatted calf, because he hath
received him safe and sound.

But he was angry, and would not go in: and his father came out, and entreated him.

But he answered and said to his father, Lo, these
many years do I serve thee, and I never trans-
gressed a commandment of thine; and yet thou
never gavest me a kid, that I might make merry
with my friends:

But when this thy son came, who hath devoured thy
living with harlots, thou killedst for him the
fatted calf.

And he said unto him, Son, thou art ever with me,
and all that is mine is thine.

But it was meet to make merry and be glad: for this
thy brother was dead, and is alive again; and
was lost, and is found.

—Luke 15: 11-32.

THE LOST SHEEP.

And He spake unto them this parable, saying,

What man of you, having a hundred sheep, and having
lost one of them, doth not leave the ninety and
nine in the wilderness, and go after that which
is lost, until he find it?

And when he hath found it, he layeth it on his shoul-
ders, rejoicing. And when he cometh home, he
calleth together his friends and his neighbors,
saying unto them, Rejoice with me, for I have
found my sheep which was lost.

I say unto you, that even so there shall be joy in heaven
over one sinner that repenteth, more than over
ninety and nine righteous persons, who need no
repentance.

—Luke 15: 3-7.

THE LOST PIECE OF SILVER.

Or what woman having ten pieces of silver, if she lose
one piece, doth not light a lamp, and sweep the
house, and seek diligently until she find it?

And when she hath found it, she calleth together her
friends and neighbors, saying, Rejoice with me,
for I have found the piece which I had lost.

Even so, I say unto you, there is joy in the pres-
ence of the angels of God over one sinner that
repenteth.
—Luke 15: 8-10.

THE WISE STEWARD.

And the Lord said, Who is then the faithful and wise
steward, whom his lord shall set over his house-
hold, to give them their portion of food in due
season?

Blessed is that servant, whom his lord when he cometh shall find so doing. Of a truth I say unto
you, that he will set him over all that he hath.

But if that servant shall say in his heart, My lord
delayeth his coming; and shall begin to beat the
menservants and the maidservants, and to eat

and drink, and to be drunken: the lord of that servant shall come in a day when he expecteth not, and in an hour when he knoweth not, and shall cut him asunder, and appoint his portion with the unfaithful.

And that servant, who knew his lord's will, and made not ready, nor did according to his will, shall be beaten with many stripes; but he that knew not, and did things worthy of stripes, shall be beaten with few stripes.

And to whomsoever much is given, of him shall much be required: and to whom they commit much, of him will they ask the more. —Luke 12: 42-48.

THE TARES

Another parable set He before them, saying, The kingdom of heaven is likened unto a man that sowed good seed in his field; but while men slept his enemy came and sowed tares also among the wheat, and went away.

But when the blade sprang up and brought forth fruit, then appeared the tares also.

And the servants of the householder came and said unto him, Sir, didst thou not sow good seed in thy field? whence then hath it tares?

And he said unto them, An enemy hath done this. And the servants say unto him, Wilt thou then that we go and gather them up?

But he saith, Nay; lest haply while ye gather up the tares, ye root up the wheat with them. Let both grow together until the harvest: and in the time of the harvest I will say to the reapers, Gather up first the tares, and bind them in bundles to burn them; but gather the wheat into my barn.

—Matt. 13: 24-30.

THE SOWER.

And when a great multitude came together, and they of every city resorted unto Him, He spake by a parable:

The sower went forth to sow his seed: and as he sowed, some fell by the wayside; and it was trodden under foot, and the birds of the heaven devoured it.

And other fell on the rock; and as soon as it grew, it withered away, because it had no moisture.

And other fell amidst the thorns; and the thorns grew with it, and choked it.

And other fell into the good ground, and grew, and

brought forth fruit a hundredfold. As He said these things, He cried, He that hath ears to hear, let him hear.

And His disciples asked Him what this parable might be.

And He said, Unto you it is given to know the mysteries of the kingdom of God: but to the rest in parables; that seeing they may not see, and hearing they may not understand.

Now the parable is this: The seed is the word of God.

And those by the wayside are they that have heard; then cometh the devil, and taketh away the word from their heart, that they may not believe and be saved.

And those on the rock are they who, when they have heard, receive the word with joy; and these have no root, who for a while believe, and in time of temptation fall away.

And that which fell among the thorns, these are they that have heard, and as they go on their way they are choked with cares and riches and pleasures of this life, and bring no fruit to perfection.

And that in the good ground, these are such as in an honest and good heart, having heard the word, hold it fast, and bring forth fruit with patience.

—Luke 8: 4-15.

THE UNJUST STEWARD.

And He said also unto the disciples, There was a certain rich man, who had a steward; and the same was accused unto him that he was wasting his goods.

And he called him, and said unto him, What is this that I hear of thee? render the account of thy stewardship; for thou canst be no longer steward.

And the steward said within himself, What shall I do, seeing that my lord taketh away the stewardship from me? I have not strength to dig; to beg I am ashamed.

I am resolved what to do, that, when I am put out of the stewardship, they may receive me into their houses.

And calling to him each one of his lord's debtors, he said to the first, How much owest thou unto my lord?

And he said, A hundred measures of oil. And he said unto him, Take thy bond, and sit down quickly and write fifty.

Then said he to another, And how much owest thou? And he said, A hundred measures of wheat. He saith unto him, Take thy bond, and write four-score.

And his lord commended the unrighteous steward because he had done wisely: for the sons of this world are for their own generation wiser than the sons of the light.

And I say unto you, Make to yourselves friends by means of the mammon of unrighteousness; that, when it shall fail, they may receive you into the eternal tabernacles.

He that is faithful in a very little is faithful also in much: and he that is unrighteous in a very little is unrighteous also in much.

If therefore ye have not been faithful in the unrighteous mammon, who will commit to your trust the true riches?

And if ye have not been faithful in that which is another's, who will give you that which is your own?

No servant can serve two masters: for either he will hate the one, and love the other; or else he will hold to one, and despise the other. Ye cannot serve God and mammon.

And the Pharisees, who were lovers of money, heard all these things; and they scoffed at him.

And he said unto them, Ye are they that justify yourselves in the sight of men; but God knoweth
your hearts: for that which is exalted among
men is an abomination in the sight of God.

The law and the prophets were until John: from that
time the gospel of the kingdom of God is
preached, and every man entereth violently
into it.

But it is easier for heaven and earth to pass away,
than for one tittle of the law to fall.

—Luke 16: 1-17.

THE UNMERCIFUL SERVANT.

Therefore is the kingdom of heaven likened unto a
certain king, who would make a reckoning with
his servants.　And when he had begun to
reckon, one was brought unto him, that owed
ten thousand talents.　But forasmuch as he had
not wherewith to pay, his lord commanded him
to be sold, and his wife, and children, and all that
he had, and payment to be made.

The servant therefore fell down and worshipped him,
saying, Lord, have patience with me, and I will
pay thee all.　And the lord of that servant, being

moved with compassion, released him, and forgave him the debt.

But that servant went out, and found one of his fellow-servants, who owed him a hundred shillings: and he laid hold on him, and took him by the throat, saying, Pay what thou owest. So the fellow-servant fell down and besought him, saying, Have patience with me, and I will pay thee. And he would not: but went and cast him into prison, till he should pay that which was due. So when his fellow-servants saw what was done, they were exceeding sorry, and came and told unto their lord all that was done.

Then his lord called him unto him, and saith to him, Thou wicked servant, I forgave thee all thy debt, because thou besoughtest me: shouldest not thou also have had mercy on thy fellow-servant, even as I had mercy on thee?

And his lord was wroth, and delivered him to the tormentors, till he should pay all that was due.

So shall also my heavenly Father do unto you, if ye forgive not every one his brother from your hearts.

—Matt. 18: 23-34.

THE TEN VIRGINS.

Then shall the kingdom of heaven be likened unto ten
virgins, who took their lamps, and went forth to
meet the bridegroom. And five of them were
foolish and five were wise. For the foolish, when
they took their lamps, took no oil with them: but
the wise took oil in their vessels with their lamps.
Now while the bridegroom tarried, they all slumbered
and slept. But at midnight there is a cry, Behold, the bridegroom! Come ye forth to meet him.
Then all those virgins arose, and trimmed their lamps.
And the foolish said unto the wise, Give us of
your oil; for our lamps are going out. But the
wise answered, saying, Peradventure there will
not be enough for us and you: go ye rather to
them that sell, and buy for yourselves.
And while they went away to buy, the bridegroom
came; and they that were ready went in with
him to the marriage feast: and the door was
shut. Afterward came also the other virgins,
saying, Lord, Lord, open to us. But he answered and said, Verily, I say unto you, I know
you not.
Watch therefore, for ye know not the day nor the
hour. —Matt. 25: 1-13.

163

JESUS AND A RICH YOUNG MAN

One time when Jesus had been teaching His disciples
and had just finished a great lesson, He started
out into the road, and, as he went along, a young
man came running and kneeled right in front
of Him.

One could tell by looking at the young man that he
was very wealthy, for his clothing was of the
finest quality. As he kneeled in front of Jesus
he eagerly looked into His loving face as
he said, "Good Teacher, what shall I do that I
may interit eternal life?" Perhaps the young
man realized that he had missed something in
his life, and that there were certain good things
that he might do to win eternal life.

Jesus turned and said to the young man: "Why callest
thou me good? There is none good save One,
even God. Thou knowest the commandments:
Do not kill, Do not commit adultery, Do not
steal, Do not bear false witness, Do not de-
fraud, Honor thy father and thy mother."

The young man expected some such answer as this
from Jesus, and he was very glad, no doubt,

that he could look right into His face and say,
"All these things have I observed from my
youth."

The young man thought he was almost perfect, and
yet he was not satisfied that he was doing everything that he should do. As Jesus looked upon
him He loved the young man, but He knew there
was something else that the young man had neg-
lected, and He said to the rich young ruler: "One
thing thou lackest; go, sell what thou hast and
give to the poor, and thou shalt have treasure in
heaven. And, come, follow Me."

When Jesus said this the young man was not
quite so happy as he had been. His riches
were his idol. Perhaps he thought he could
serve both God and mammon, and the story
says that because he had great possessions
his countenance fell and he went away sor-
rowful.

There is nothing recorded in the Bible that tells what
became of the young man, but it does say: "And
Jesus looked round about, and saith unto His
disciples, How hardly shall they that have riches
enter into the kingdom of God!'

And the disciples were amazed at His words. But
Jesus answereth again, and saith unto them:
"Children, how hard it is for them that trust in
riches to enter into the kingdom of God."

JEHOVAH ABOVE ALL

Jehovah reigneth; He is clothed with majesty;
Jehovah is clothed with strength;
He hath girded Himself therewith:
The world also is established, that it cannot be moved.
Thy throne is established of old:
Thou art from everlasting.

The floods have lifted up, O Jehovah,
The floods have lifted up their voice;
The floods lift up their waves.

Above the voices of many waters,
The mighty breakers of the sea,
Jehovah on high is mighty.

Thy testimonies are very sure:
Holiness becometh Thy house,
O Jehovah, for evermore.   —Psalm 93.

HOSANNA

Hosanna! loud hosanna!
  The little children sang;
Thro' pillared court and temple
  The glorious anthem rang:
To Jesus Who had blessed them,
  Close folded to His breast,
The children sang their praises
  The simplest and the best.

From Olivet they followed,
  'Midst an exultant crowd,
Waving the victor palmbranch,
  And shouting clear and loud;
Bright angels joined the chorus
  Beyond the cloudless sky—
"Hosanna in the highest:
  Glory to God on high!"

Fair leaves of silvery olive
  They strewed upon the ground,
Whilst Salem's circling mountains
  Echoed the joyous sound;
The Lord of men and angels
  Rode on in lowly state,
Nor scorned that little children
  Should on His bidding wait.

"Hosanna in the highest!"
  That ancient song we sing;
For Christ is our Redeemer—
  The Lord of heaven—our King.

—Jeannette Threlfall.

169

153

170

A GIFT THAT PLEASED JESUS

It was the last week of Jesus' life on earth. He had journeyed up to Jerusalem knowing that He would soon be in the hands of His enemies, but He did not sit down and mourn and lament. He was at work almost every minute of the time. There were many lessons to be taught; there were many sick to be healed; there were all sorts of questions for Him to answer.

Jesus was in the great temple on Tuesday of this last week in His life. He had sat down over against the treasury, and as He was sitting there He watched the people put their offerings into the chest.

It was a very easy matter to note how the people did this, for the chest was in the hall, or court, of the temple, fastened to the side, and as the people passed by, they dropped their offerings into it.

As Jesus was sitting there many people who had plenty came by and carelessly tossed their offerings into the chest. It was no unusual thing for the chest to contain so much that it could not all be used in defraying the expenses of the building, and the

171

wealthy people were always very lavish in their giving.

But somebody altogether different came by. That somebody was a poor widow who had only two mites. Jesus watched her as she approached the treasury; He watched her as she placed in it all the money that she had. He also saw that she did not do this grudgingly.

Jesus very quietly called His disciples to Him, and this is what He said to them: "Verily, I say unto you, This poor widow cast in more than all they that are casting into the treasury: for they all did cast in of their superfluity; but she of her want did cast in all that she had, even all her living."

-------------✧-------------

"Not what we give, but what we share,
For the gift without the giver is bare."

—*Lowell.*

-------------✧-------------

A thing of beauty is a joy forever:
Its loveliness increases; it never
Passes into nothingness; but still will keep
A bower quiet for us, and sleep
Full of sweet dreams, health and quiet breathing.

—*Keats.*

SUN OF MY SOUL

Sun of my soul, Thou Saviour dear,
It is not night if Thou be near;
O may no earth-born cloud arise
To hide Thee from Thy servant's eyes.

When the soft dews of kindly sleep
My wearied eyelids gently steep,
Be my last thought, how sweet to rest
Forever on my Saviour's breast.

Be near to bless me when I wake,
Ere through the world my way I take;
Abide with me till in Thy love
I lose myself in heaven above.

—*John Kepler.*

174

THE VINE AND THE BRANCHES

I am the true vine, and My Father is the husbandman.

Every branch in Me that beareth not fruit, He taketh
it away: and every branch that beareth fruit, He
cleanseth it, that it may bear more fruit.

Already ye are clean because of the word which I
have spoken unto you.

Abide in Me, and I in you. As the branch cannot
bear fruit of itself, except it abide in the vine; so
neither can ye, except ye abide in Me.

I am the vine, ye are the branches: he that abideth
in Me, and I in him, the same beareth much fruit:
for apart from Me ye can do nothing.

If a man abide not in Me, he is cast forth as a branch
and is withered; and they gather them, and cast
them into the fire, and they are burned.

If ye abide in Me, and My words abide in you, ask
whatsoever ye will, and it shall be done unto you.

Herein is My Father glorified, that ye bear much
fruit; and so shall ye be My disciples.

Even as the Father hath loved Me, I also have loved
you: abide ye in My love.

If ye keep My commandments, ye shall abide in My love; even as I have kept My Father's commandments, and abide in His love.

These things have I spoken unto you, that My joy may be in you, and that your joy may be made full.

This is My commandment, that ye love one another, even as I have loved you.

Greater love hath no man than this, that a man lay down his life for his friends.

Ye are My friends, if ye do the things which I command you.

No longer do I call you servants; for the servant knoweth not what his lord doeth: but I have called you friends; for all things that I heard from My Father I have made known unto you.

Ye did not choose Me, but I chose you and appointed you, that ye should go and bear fruit, and that your fruit should abide: that whatsoever ye shall ask of the Father in My name He may give it you.

These things I command you, that ye may love one another.

—John 15: 1-17.

THE BUILDERS

All are architects of Fate,
  Working in these walls of Time;
Some with massive deeds and great,
  Some with ornaments of rhyme.

Nothing useless is, or low;
  Each thing in its place is best;
And what seems but idle show
  Strengthens and supports the rest.

For the structure that we raise
  Time is with materials filled;
Our to-days and yesterdays
  Are the blocks with which we build.

Truly shape and fasten these;
  Leave no yawning gaps between;
Think not, because no man sees,
  Such things will remain unseen.

In the elder days of art,
　　Builders wrought with greatest care
Each minute and unseen part;
　　For the gods see everywhere.

Let us do our work as well,
　　Both the unseen and the seen;
Make the house where God may dwell
　　Beautiful, entire and clean.

Else our lives are incomplete,
　　Standing in these walls of Time:
Broken stairways, where the feet
　　Stumble as they seek to climb.

Build to-day, then, strong and sure,
　　With a firm and ample base;
And ascending and secure
　　Shall to-morrow find its place.

Thus alone can we attain
　　To those turrets where the eye
Sees the world as one vast plain,
　　And one boundless reach of sky.

—Henry W. Longfellow.

THE CRUCIFIXION FORETOLD

Who hath believed our message? and to whom hath
the arm of Jehovah been revealed?

For He grew up before Him as a tender plant, and as
a root out of a dry ground: He hath no form nor
comeliness; and when we see Him, there is no
beauty that we should desire Him.

He was despised, and rejected of men; a Man of sorrows, and acquainted with grief: and as one
from whom men hide their face He was despised
and we esteemed Him not.

Surely He hath borne our griefs, and carried our
sorrows; yet we did esteem Him stricken, smitten of God, and afflicted.

But He was wounded for our transgressions, He was
bruised for our iniquities; the chastisement of
our peace was upon Him; and with His stripes
we are healed.

All we like sheep have gone astray; we have turned
every one to his own way; and Jehovah hath
laid on Him the iniquity of us all.

He was oppressed, yet when He was afflicted He
opened not his mouth; as a lamb that is led to

the slaughter, and as a sheep that before its shearer is dumb, so He opened not His mouth.

By oppression and judgment He was taken away; and as for His generation, who among them considered that He was cut off out of the land of the living for the transgression of my people to whom the stroke was due?

And they made His grave with the wicked, and with a rich man in His death; although He had done no violence, neither was any deceit in His mouth.

—Isa. 53: 1-9.

JESUS' FAREWELL PRAYER

These things spake Jesus; and lifting up His eyes to
heaven, He said, Father, the hour is come; glorify
Thy Son, that the Son may glorify Thee:

Even as Thou gavest Him authority over all flesh,
that to all whom Thou hast given Him, He should
give eternal life.

And this is life eternal, that they should know Thee
the only true God, and Him whom Thou didst send,
even Jesus Christ.

I glorified Thee on the earth, having accomplished the
work which Thou hast given Me to do.

And now, Father, glorify Thou Me with Thine own
self with the glory which I had with Thee before
the world was.

I manifested Thy name unto the men whom Thou gavest Me out of the world: Thine they were, and
Thou gavest them to Me; and they have kept Thy
word.

Now they know that all things whatsoever Thou hast
given Me are from Thee:

For the words which Thou gavest Me I have given
unto them; and they received them, and knew of

a truth that I came forth from Thee, and they believed that Thou didst send Me.

I pray for them: I pray not for the world, but for those whom Thou hast given Me; for they are Thine:

And all things that are Mine and Thine and Thine are Mine: and I am glorified in them.

And I am no more in the world, and these are in the world, and I come to Thee. Holy Father, keep them in Thy name which Thou hast given Me, that they may be one, even as we are.

While I was with them, I kept them in Thy name which Thou hast given Me: and I guarded them, and not one of them perished, but the son of perdition; that the scripture might be fulfilled.

But now I come to Thee; and these things I speak in the world, that they may have My joy made full in themselves.

I have given them Thy word; and the world hated them, because they are not of the world, even as I am not of the world.

I pray not that Thou shouldest take them from the world, but that Thou shouldest keep them from the evil one.

They are not of the world, even as I am not of the world.

Sanctify them in the truth: Thy word is truth.

As Thou didst send Me into the world, even so sent I them into the world.

And for their sakes I sanctify Myself, that they themselves also may be sanctified in truth.

Neither for these only do I pray, but for them also that believe on Me through their word;

That they may all be one; even as Thou, Father, art in Me, and I in Thee, that they also may be in us: that the world may believe that Thou didst send Me.

And the glory which Thou hast given Me I have given unto them; that they may be one, even as We are one;

I in them, and Thou in Me, that they may be perfected into one; that the world may know that Thou didst send Me, and lovedst them, even as Thou lovedst Me.

Father, I desire that they also whom Thou hast given Me be with Me where I am, that they may behold My glory, which Thou hast given Me: for Thou lovedst Me before the foundation of the world.

O righteous Father, the world knew Thee not, but I
knew Thee; and these knew that Thou didst
send me;

And I made known unto them Thy name, and will
make it known; that the love wherewith Thou
lovedst Me may be in them, and I in them.

When Jesus had spoken these words, He went forth
with His disciples over the brook Kidron, where
was a garden, into which He entered, Himself
and His disciples.

—John 17: 1—18: 1.

A VOICE UPON THE MIDNIGHT AIR

A Voice upon the midnight air,
  Where Kidron's moonlit waters stray,
Weeps forth in agony of prayer,
  "Oh Father, take this cup away."

O King of earth, the cross ascend;
  O'er climes and ages 'tis Thy throne.
Where'er Thy fading eye may bend,
  The desert blooms and is Thine own.

—*James Martineau.*

185

THE GARDEN PRAYER

And when He was at the place He said unto them,
    Pray that ye enter not into temptation.
And He was parted from them about a stone's cast;
    and He kneeled down and prayed, saying, Father,
    if Thou be willing remove this cup from Me:
    nevertheless not My will, but Thine, be done.
And there appeared unto Him an angel from heaven,
    strengthening Him.
And being in an agony He prayed more earnestly;
    and His sweat became as it were, great drops of
    blood falling down upon the ground.
And when He rose up from His prayer, He came
    unto the disciples and saw them sleeping for
    sorrow.
And said unto them, Why sleep ye? rise and pray,
    that ye enter not into temptation.

'Tis midnight, and on Olive's brow,
    The Star is dimmed that lately shone:
'Tis midnight in the garden now,
    The suffering Saviour prays alone.

'Tis midnight; and from ether plains
    Is borne the song that angels know:
Unheard by mortals are the strains
    That sweetly soothe the Saviour's woe.

THE BETRAYAL

Now Judas also, who betrayed Him, knew the place:
for Jesus oft-times resorted thither with His disciples.

Judas then, having received the band of soldiers, and
officers from the chief priests and the Pharisees,
cometh thither with lanterns and torches and
weapons.

Jesus therefore, knowing all the things that were
coming upon Him, went forth, and saith unto
them, Whom seek ye?

They answered Him, Jesus of Nazareth. Jesus saith
unto them, I am He. And Judas also, who betrayed Him, was standing with them.

When therefore He said unto them, I am He, they
went backward, and fell to the ground.

Again therefore He asked them, Whom seek ye? And
they said, Jesus of Nazareth.

Jesus answered, I told you that I am He; if therefore
ye seek Me, let these go their way:

That the word might be fulfilled which He spake, of
those whom Thou hast given Me I lost not one.

Simon Peter therefore having a sword drew it, and

struck the high priest's servant, and cut off his
right ear. Now the servant's name was Malchus.
Jesus therefore said unto Peter, Put up the sword into
the sheath: the cup which the Father hath given
Me, shall I not drink it?
So the band and the chief captain, and the officers of
the Jews, seized Jesus and bound Him.

—John 18: 2-12.

CHRIST BEFORE PILATE

Now Jesus stood before the governor: and the governor asked Him, saying, Art Thou the King of the Jews? And Jesus said unto him, Thou sayest.

And when He was accused by the chief priests and elders, He answered nothing.

Then saith Pilate unto Him, Hearest Thou not how many things they witness against Thee?

And He gave him no answer, not even to one word: insomuch that the governor marvelled greatly.

Now at the feast the governor was wont to release unto the multitude one prisoner, whom they would.

And they had then a notable prisoner, called Barabbas. When therefore they were gathered together, Pilate said unto them, Whom will ye that I release unto you? Barabbas, or Jesus who is called Christ?

For he knew that for envy they had delivered Him up.

And while he was sitting on the judgment-seat, his wife sent unto him, saying, Have thou nothing to do with that righteous man; for I have suffered many things this day in a dream because of Him.

Now the chief priests and the elders persuaded the multitudes that they should ask for Barabbas, and destroy Jesus.

But the governor answered and said unto them, Which of the two will ye that I release unto you? And they said, Barabbas.

Pilate saith unto them, What then shall I do unto Jesus who is called Christ? They all say, Let Him be crucified.

And he said, Why, what evil hath He done? But they cried out exceedingly, saying, Let Him be crucified.

So when Pilate saw that he prevailed nothing, but rather that a tumult was arising, he took water, and washed his hands before the multitude, saying, I am innocent of the blood of this righteous man; see ye to it.

And all the people answered and said, His blood be us, and on our children.

Then released he unto them Barabbas; but Jesus he scourged and delivered to be crucified.

—Matt. 27: 1, 2, 11-26.

192

THE MOCKERY

Then the soldiers of the governor took Jesus into the
Prætorium, and gathered unto Him the whole
band,

And they stripped Him, and put on him a scarlet
robe,

And they platted a crown of thorns and put it upon
His head, and a reed in His right hand; and
they kneeled down before Him, and mocked
Him, saying, Hail, King of the Jews!

And they spat upon Him, and took the reed and smote
Him on the head.

And when they had mocked Him, they took off from
Him the robe, and put on Him His garments, and
led Him away to crucify Him.

And as they came out, they found a man of Cyrene,
Simon by name: him they compelled to go with
them, that he might bear His cross.

And when they were come unto a place called Gol-
gotha, that is to say, The place of a skull,

They gave Him wine to drink mingled with gall: and
when He had tasted it, He would not drink.

And when they had crucified Him, they parted His
garments among them, casting lots;

And they sat and watched Him there.

And they set up over His head His accusation written, THIS IS JESUS, THE KING OF THE
JEWS.

Then are there crucified with Him two robbers, one
on the right hand and one on the left.

And they that passed by railed on Him, wagging their
heads,

And saying, Thou that destroyest the temple, and
buildest it in three days, save Thyself: if Thou
art the Son of God, come down from the cross.

In like manner also the chief priests mocking Him,
with the scribes and elders, said,

He saved others; Himself He cannot save. He is the
King of Israel; let Him now come down from the
cross, and we will believe on Him.

He trusteth on God; let Him deliver Him now, if He
desireth Him: for He said, I am the Son of
God.

And the robbers also that were crucified with Him
cast upon Him the same reproach.

—Matt. 27: 27-44.

194

THE RISEN LORD

Our Lord is risen from the dead,
    Our Jesus is gone up on high;
The powers of hell are captive led,
    Dragged to the portals of the sky.
There His triumphal chariot waits,
    And angels chant the solemn lay:
"Lift up your heads, ye heavenly gates!
    Ye everlasting doors, give way!"

Loose all your bars of massy light,
And wide unfold the ethereal scene:
He claims these mansions as His right;
Receive the King of glory in.
Who is this King of glory—who?
The Lord who all our foes o'ercame;
Who sin, and death, and hell o'erthrew;
And Jesus is the conqueror's name.

Lo! His triumphal chariot waits,
And angels chant the solemn lay:—
"Lift up your heads, ye heavenly gates!
Ye everlasting doors, give way!"
Who is this King of glory—who?
The Lord of boundless power possessed;
The King of saints and angels, too,
God over all, for ever blessed.

—*Charles Wesley.*

———————❖———————

Scarce morning twilight had begun
To chase the shades of night away,
When Christ arose—unsetting Sun—
The dawn of joy's eternal day.

HOLY, HOLY, HOLY

Reginald Heber.

Rev. John B. Dykes.

1. Ho-ly, Ho-ly, Ho-ly, Lord God Al-might-y! Ear-ly in the
2. Ho-ly, Ho-ly, Ho-ly! All the saints a-dore Thee, Cast-ing down their
3. Ho-ly, Ho-ly, Ho-ly! Tho' the darkness hide Thee, Tho' the eye of
4. Ho-ly, Ho-ly, Ho-ly, Lord God Al-might-y! All Thy works shall

morn - ing our song shall rise to Thee; Ho-ly, Ho-ly, Ho-ly!
gold-en crowns a-round the glass-y sea; Cher-u-bim and ser-a-phim
sin-ful man Thy glo-ry may not see, On-ly Thou art ho-ly;
praise Thy name, in earth, and sky, and sea; Ho-ly, Ho-ly, Ho-ly!

Mer - ci - ful and Might-y! God in Three Per-sons, blessed Trin-i-ty!
fall-ing down be-fore Thee, Who wert, and art, and ev-er-more shalt be.
there is none be-side Thee Per-fect in pow'r, in love, and pu-ri-ty.
Mer - ci - ful and Might-y! God in Three Per-sons, blessed Trin-i-ty! A-MEN.

198

JERUSALEM THE GOLDEN

(Poem nearly eight hundred years old.)

Jerusalem the golden!
  With milk and honey blest,
Beneath thy contemplation
  Sink heart and voice oppress'd.
I know not—oh, I know not,
  What joys await me there.
What radiancy of glory,
  What bliss beyond compare.

They stand, those halls of Zion
  All jubilant with song,
And bright with many an angel,
  And all the martyred throng.
There is the throne of David,
  And there from toil released,
The shout of them that triumph
  The song of them that feast.

And they who with their Leader
  Have conquered in the fight,
Forever and forever
  Are clad in robes of white.
Oh, land that see'st no sorrow!
  Oh, state that fearest no strife!
Oh, royal land of flowers!
  Oh, realm and home of life!

Oh, sweet and blessed country,
  The home of God's elect!
Oh, sweet and blessed country,
  That eager hearts expect!
Jesus, in mercy bring us
  T' that dear land of rest!
Who art with God the Father,
  And Spirit ever blest.
                              —*Bernard of Cluny.*

FAITH OF OUR FATHERS

Frederick W. Faber.

Ad. by J. G. Walton.

1, Faith of our fa - thers! liv - ing still, In spite of dun-geon, fire and sword:
2. Our fa-thers, chained in pris-ons dark, Were still in heart and conscience free;
3. Faith of our fa - thers! we will love Both friend and foe in all our strife:

O how our hearts beat high with joy Whene'er we hear that glo - rious word!
How sweet would be their children's fate, If they, like them, could die for thee!
And preach thee, too, as love knows how, By kind-ly words and vir - tuous life:

Faith of our Fa - thers! ho - ly faith! We will be true to thee till death!
Faith of our Fa - thers! ho - ly faith! We will be true to thee till death!
Faith of our Fa - thers! ho - ly faith! We will be true to thee till death!

GOOD TO REMEMBER

I said, I will take heed to my ways,
That I sin not with my tongue;
I will keep my mouth with a bridle,
While the wicked is before me.
I was dumb with silence, I held my peace.

He that hideth hatred is of lying lips;
And he that uttereth a slander is a fool.
In the multitude of words there wanteth not trans-
    gression;
But he that refraineth his lips doeth wisely.

The tongue of the righteous is as choice silver:
The heart of the wicked is little worth.
The lips of the righteous feed many;
But the foolish die for lack of understanding.

He that hath a wayward heart findeth no good;
And he that hath a perverse tongue falleth into mis-
    chief.

A fool's lips enter into contention,
And his mouth calleth for stripes.

A fool's mouth is his destruction,
And his lips are the snare of his soul.

He that guardeth his mouth keepeth his life;
But he that openeth wide his lips shall have destruc-
    tion.

A righteous man hateth lying;
But a wicked man is loathsome and cometh to shame.

Better is the poor that walketh in his integrity
Than he that is perverse in his lips and is a fool.

A soft answer turneth away wrath;
But a grievous word stirreth up anger.

A gentle tongue is a tree of life;
But perverseness therein is a breaking of the spirit.

The lips of the wise disperse knowledge;
But the heart of the foolish doeth not so.

A man hath joy in the answer of his mouth;
And a work in due season, how good it is!

—*The Bible.*

205

206

LIST OF BIBLICAL WORDS

For convenience, we append this list of Biblical names. Authority for pronunciation is the new American Standard Revised Version of the Bible.

Aaron—aâr'on.
Abarim—ăb'a-rĭm.
Abishai—a-bĭsh'a-ī.
Abraham—ā'bra-ham.
Absalom—ăb'sa-lom.
Adonijah—ăd'o-nī'jah.
Adonizedek—a-dō'ni-zē'dek.
Adullam—a-dŭl'lam.
Ahimaaz—a-hĭm'a-ăz.
Ammon—ăm'mon.
Amorites—ăm'o-rītes.
Ashtaroth—ăsh'ta-rŏth.
Balaam—bā'laam.
Barabbas—Bär-ăb'bas.
Bashan—bā'shan.
Bedan—bē'dan.
Benaiah—be-nā'iah.
Bethlehem—bĕth'le-hem.
Canaan—cā'naan.
Cherethites—chĕr'e-thītes.
Cushites—cŭsh'ītes.
Cyrene—çy-rē'ne.
Debir—dē'bir.
Eglon—ĕg'lon.
Elijah—e-lī'jah.
Elim—ē'lim.
Ephraim—ē'phra-ĭm.
Esau—ē'sau.
Ethiop—ē'thi-ōp.
Genessaret—gen-nĕs'a-rĕt.
Geshur—ḡē'shur.
Gibeon—ḡĭb'e-on.
Gibeonites—ḡĭb'e-on-ītes.
Gihon—ḡī-hon.
Gilgal—ḡĭl'ḡăl.
Gittite—ḡĭt'tīte.
Hebron—hē'bron.
Hoham—hō'ham.
Hor—hôr.
Isaac—ī'şaac.
Israel—ĭş'ra-el.
Ittai—ĭt'ta-ī.

Jacob—jā'cob.
Japhia—ja-phī'a.
Jarmuth—jär'muth.
Jehoiada—je-hoi'a-da.
Jehovah—jē-hō'vah.
Jerub-baal—jĕ-rŭb'ba-ăl.
Jerusalem—jē-rụ'sa-lĕm.
Joab—jō'ab.
Jordan—jôr'dan.
Joshua—jŏsh'u-å.
Kadesh—kā'desh.
Keilah—kēi'lah.
Kidron—kĭd'ron.
Laban—lā'ban.
Lachish—lā'ehish.
Lebanon—lĕb'a-non.
Malchus—măl'ehus.
Meribah—mĕr'i-bah.
Mizar—mī'zar.
Moriah—mo-rī'ah.
Nahash—nā'hăsh.
Nain—nā'in.
Nathan—nā'than.
Nazareth—năz'a-rĕth.
Og—ŏg.
Olives—ŏl'ives.
Omerful—ō'mer-ful.
Palestine—păl'es-tīne.
Pelethites—pĕl'e-thītes.
Pharisees—phăr'i-sees.
Philistines—phĭ-lĭs'tĭnes.
Piram—pī'ram.
Phœnicia—phœ-nī'cia.
Rebekah—re-bĕk'ah.
Samaritan—sa-măr'i-tan.
Sheba—shē'bå.
Sinai—sī'nāi.
Sisera—sĭs'e-rå.
Solomon—sŏl'o-mon.
Zadok—zā'dok.
Zeruiah—zĕr'u-ī'ah.

208